C000084786

THE MEANING OF CANTONA

THE MEANING OF CANTONA

Meditations on Life, Art and Perfectly Weighted Balls

Terence Blacker
and
William Donaldson

MAINSTREAM
PUBLISHING

EDINBURGH AND LONDON

First published in Great Britain in 1997 by
MAINSTREAM PUBLISHING COMPANY
(EDINBURGH) LTD
7 Albany Street
Edinburgh EH1 3UG

ISBN 1 85158 950 3

A catalogue record for this book is available from the
British Library

Typeset in Garamond and Albertus
Printed and bound in Great Britain by Butler & Tanner Ltd

INTRODUCTION

The paradox, the conundrum, the overhead bicycle kick: few personalities in contemporary life embody the complexities of post-modern existence as precisely, yet as enigmatically, as Eric Cantona.

He is a Frenchman, yet his favourite meal is tripe and onions at the Rat and Carrot, Wigan.

A team member, he is never more alone than when surrounded by Keano, Giggsy and the big lad, Pallistery.

Famously reserved, he shared the intimate family occasion of his 30th birthday with readers of *Hullo!* magazine.

So, what is Cantona? Who is he? What can we learn from his life and belief systems in this, the glorious English flowering of a Frenchman's summer?

'I live so that Cantona may weave his fantasies on the park,' he has said, 'and these justify me.'

Like many great artists, Cantona habitually refers to himself in the third person, and this celebrated declaration, with its intentional echo of Borges (whom Cantona greatly admires), could lead readers to suppose that the words gathered in these pages were written by Cantona himself.

They were not. They were collected, developed and discussed by his followers, the so-called *cantonistes*, in pubs, cafés and dressing-rooms both in this country and in France. They are the Cantona which even he may not have expressed and, as such, are the purest possible reflection of the inner man.

They reveal such a profound sense of modern life that, just as Brillat-Savarin was described as *le philosophe de la cuisine* and Battaille as *le philosophe du boudoir*, Eric Cantona will surely become known as *le philosophe du parc*.

Good conversation, Cantona is rumoured to have said, is like a perfectly weighted ball into the 18-yard box. It surprises. It has a life of its own. It leaves the big lad Pearce with egg on his face. It has 'back of the net' written all over it.

Here, in these imagined conversations and biographical constructs (fictionally recreated from remarks he might have made to the lads, but almost certainly didn't), is the essence, the perfect balls, of *le philosophe du parc*.

T.B.
W.D.

University of East Anglia

1

The back streets of Marseilles, 20 years ago.
Fat women return from the market. Old
men play *boules*. A group of schoolboys
absorbed in a football game. Their excited
cries:

'Je suis Platini!'
'Je suis Pele!'
'Je suis Cruyff!'

2

The smallest, most skilful, of the boys
dribbles towards a makeshift goal. He scores.

3

'Moi? Je suis Cantona!'

4

Identity is a role we impersonate. The hero
imagines himself to greatness.

5

The smallest, most skilful, of the boys slows
the game down. He puts his foot on the ball.
Suddenly he bends it between a bicycle and
a litter-bin, and scores another goal.

6

'Rapid Vienna 0! Manchester United 2!'

7

'Quoi?' The old men pause in their game.
'Manchester United?' Who is this skilful boy
with his strange dreams? And why does he
wear his collar up?

8

Cantona wears his collar up? *Non!* Others
wear their collars down.

9

In matters of the beautiful game, the child is father to the man. The child who learns to play on a pitch, in a park, on a lawn, discovers control, discipline, tight passing. The child who learns on the streets discovers the football of freedom: channels, one-way streets, pedestrian crossings, oncoming traffic, running into space. His is the apprenticeship of privilege.

10

A Sartrean conundrum. The average footballer grows to love his prison. The great footballer is condemned to be free.

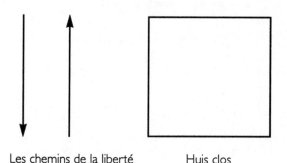

Les chemins de la liberté   Huis clos

11

The years pass. The cygnet has become a
swan. Eric Cantona – hero of Marseilles and
France.

12

At home to Nîmes. Cantona asks many
searching questions of the visitors' defence.

13

'Argue me this, Henri. If death is not an
event in life, why do we fear it so?'

14

'*Comment*, Eric?'

15

Un nul!

16

No man is a hypocrite in his own pleasures.
And the greatest pleasure? The joys of a
private life? The turning of an interesting
thought? The composition of a fine
painting? Of course. But beyond that – the
scoring of a goal.

17

Cantona asks further searching questions of the Nîmes defence. 'Here's one, Henri! What must have the force of truth must not be true. To enact anger one must not be angry. So, to enact greatness, must one not be great?'

18

'Faire quoi?'

19

Deux nul!

20

The world is at his feet. And yet. Who knows the world who only Marseilles knows?

21

The provincial actor hears only clapping hands. He is deaf to the drumbeat of distant challenges. Sooner or later, the heroic actor must leave the provinces and test himself in the greatest roles.

22

It is not that the ordinary man cannot imagine. It is that the exceptional man imagines more.

23

Cantona plays the beautiful game as Monet painted. As the songbird sings.

24

And yet it is not enough.

25

Monet and the beautiful game. What makes *Les Champs en hiver, 1887* remarkable is not the individual colours. It is the way the individual colours combine to make great art.

26

Compare this with the French football team. Colombard, Papin, Gaston, Lebec, Ginola? Splashes of colour which dazzle but which offend the eye.

27

The business of great art is to adapt the classical, to subsume the individual experience to the universal. And the European style of football? The classicist must be sickened by its gaudy *pointillism*, by its infantile need to break with tradition, by its onanistic emphasis on individual skill.

28

When French players arrive at a game it is in their sponsored wire-wheeled Porsches and Mercedes. They are dressed like brightly coloured butterflies. They compete for our attention like street pimps in a boulevard farce.

29

It is said that when the French team attended a performance of *Guys and Dolls* at London's National Theatre, they were redirected to the *artistes'* entrance.

30

Cantona has studied the English game. In England, players arrive together on a coach. They wear identical suits and club ties, like a group of trainee salesmen on a works outing. In England, the individual is subsumed to the universal.

31

After an away game, a French player breaks away from the group to explore this new environment. He strolls round the unfamiliar town, he meets new people, he discusses *la condition humaine* with strangers in the local square. He stays overnight. The next day, he returns for training – curiously diminished.

32

After an away game, the English player is given a pre-packed hamburger and is put back on the bus, as if he might be infected by the alien air. Thus, he returns from every away game strengthened, even more himself.

33

A French player's team: his wife, his
girlfriend, his agent, his accountant, his
hairdresser, his media liaison adviser.

34

An English player's team: the lads.

35

Only as part of a team can a man find his
true identity. To survive alone, the wolf must
learn to run with the pack.

36

Cantona is strangely dissatisfied. He
continues to weave his fantasies on the field
– but as if from memory. Off the field, the
fantasies wither and die. At home, in his
study, he takes up his pen, but the verses
refuse to flow. He begins a haiku – his
preferred discipline. *'France! Mon pays . . .'*
Nothing! *Mon pays quoi?* Nothing can be
completed. He seeks professional help.

37

The footballer in therapy? A contradiction?
Hardly. No one can be a whole player if he
is only half a man, if his spirit is only half
formed. On the pitch, his play lacks
completion. Off the pitch, he cannot (he
will not) complete his sentences.

38

A speech therapist's consulting-room. 'You
appear to reject the trivial, suburban
neatness of the subject-verb-object sentence,
M. Cantona. You find unacceptable the
essentially bourgeois and aptly named
subordinate clause.'

39

Cantona explains. 'Which of the following
sentences is the most true:

40

"To deprive a man of his vices is to strip a
tree of its bark: the appearance is tidier, the
result extinction." Or:

41

"To deprive a man of his vices is to strip a tree of its bark." Or:

42

"To deprive a man of."

43

'Each has its merits. Only one confers upon the listener the privilege of closure.'

44

The therapist studies the case and delivers his verdict.

45

'Your sentences lack completion,
M. Cantona, because, in a very real sense, your life lacks completion.'

46

'An interesting verdict, *monsieur*. All is much clearer now that you have explained it to me.'

47

The therapist is delighted. '*Mais voilà!* A perfect sentence. You are cured, M. Cantona!'

48

'How much do.'

49

'*Merde!*'

50

Why does a life lack completion? Cantona observes the French game: its chairman playing politics; its fans feigning indifference; its players more concerned with pleasing themselves, their agents, their *petites amies* in the executive box, than playing their part in a team. For them, style is all. Victory and truth are nothing.

51
Cantona reaches a conclusion.

52
Irony —

53
Irony is —

54
Irony is killing —

55
Irony is killing football.

56

Completion! In an age of irony, of *le cool*, it no longer matters whether you are authentic, sincere, a winner; whether you behave honourably or dishonourably. Appearance is all. Not, 'How did I do, boss?', but, 'How did I look, *cherie?*'

57

During the next game, a friendly against Torpedo Moscow, Cantona also finds completion on the pitch. The fans are whistling ironically. The players are ironically playing '*foot-pissoir*'. Cantona's frustration grows. He kicks the ball into the crowd. They laugh ironically. When he is substituted, he is winked at by the referee. '*Au vélo*, Canto,' he says.

58

Cantona is gripped by an icy rage. Even the referee is being ironic! In that moment, Cantona makes a gesture that will, for all time, expose the emptiness of these post-modern self-abusers.

59

He takes off his shirt and stamps on it.

60

The end of irony. Completion.

61

What of the English? It is not that the English do not understand irony. It is that they have seen it in all its amoral emptiness and rejected it. Their beloved Nobbies and Robbos and Charlos were great players precisely because, in order to be truly themselves, to be more truly part of a team, they cast off the leering, antic demons of self-mockery.

62

England is a country uncontaminated by the European disease of post-modern irony, the rabies of the soul.

63

In France, the sober post-match analysis of Trevor Brooking would be considered too serious to be serious. Greavesie would be a national treasure.

64

But then in France, on national television, there is a game show entitled *Ils pensent que c'est tout au dessus*, in which blindfolded sporting celebrities – to the accompaniment of ribald comments by bald comedians – identify each other by touching one another up. In England, such a thing could never happen.

65

The Englishman dares to be dull. It is his strength. In England a grey man in a blazer is wisely put in authority. The Englishman looks at Graham Kelly and he feels intelligent. He sees John Major and he is witty. He listens to Harry Redknapp and he is Voltaire.

66

To be fair, David Pleat leaves him puzzled.

67

Only tuneless birds, inarticulate warriors, need bright plumage.

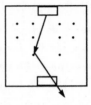

Between the futile foreplay of Marseilles and the
over-enthusiastic premature ejaculation of
Wimbledon, the perfect act of love is to be found.

68

There is a saying in France: *'Je suis tout droit,
Jacques.'* You won't hear that in England.

69

The cucumber would do well to remember
that a salad is more than the sum of its parts.

70

The heroic actor must be challenged in the
greatest roles. True. But he is part of an
ensemble. He is the servant of the text.
Hamlet without Horatio? The bombastic
Moor without his scheming corporal?

71

Gallic indiscipline. The celebrated theatrical scandal of 1948. At the *Comédie Française*, Jean-Louis Barrault and Louis Jouvet are to alternate the roles of Othello and Iago. The boulevards hum with excitement.

72

On the opening night, Barrault is Othello, Jouvet Iago. Triumph! The critics are ecstatic! On the second night, Jouvet is Othello, Barrault Iago. Another triumph! The critics run out of superlatives.

73

The third performance is a matinée. Before it, Barrault and Jouvet celebrate their joint triumph over lunch. They have a cognac. Then another. Then a third, and then they have a matinée.

74

They return to the theatre, and both play Iago. The audience applaud. They have noticed nothing unusual. In London, such a thing could never happen.

75

The Frenchman's insularity. He fears the foreign, yet longs for it, as an ageing virgin fears yet longs for love. It is not the commitment of Tony Adams, the foot swiftness of Gary Lineker, the square balls of Ray 'Butch' Wilkins that make them adored in France. It is their non-Frenchness.

76

That said, Rushy's Italian adventure ended in heartbreak.

77

A telegram arrives from England. 'The male peacock needs an open stage for its displays.' It is signed – Wilko of Leeds.

78

The ultimate challenge! An invitation to play the beautiful game in the finest league in the world! The Premiership!

79

The haikus flow again.

80

Haiku 1
'Derry and Toms. Tim
Rice and Anita Dobson.
They'll do for me, John.'

81

But Cantona will not be rushed. He
considers carefully. The hasty sprat repents at
leisure. Wisee monkey catchee mackerel.

82

We are what we play. The Frenchman
seduces the ball. The Italian renders it a
minor work of art. The German organises it.
And the Englishman? He kicks it very hard
and then spits on the ground in
disappointment. Only the Englishman truly
cares.

83

Michel Platini has observed that in France
we have spectators, in England they have
fans. In France, spectators watch the
beautiful game. In England, the fan sees the
tragedy of his life enacted on the park. Long
throw. Route one. Late tackle. Red card.
Well gutted.

84

A theory of history. Great events are destined
to repeat themselves, but the scale of them
will change. Only in the mud and attrition
of some fog-bound local derby in the north
do we see the controlled hooliganism of
England's imperial past – the spirit of
Rourkes's Drift and Paschendale, of Raleigh
and Hawkins and Drake, of Cook and Wolfe
and the great Victorian adventurers.

85

'Take my drum to England,
Hang it by the shore,
Strike it when your powder's runnin' low;
If the Dons sight Devon,
I'll quit the port o' Heaven,
An' drum them up the Channel
As we drummed them long ago.'

86

'Bag o' shite! Bag o' shite! Bag o' shite! Come and have a go if you think you're hard enough!'

87

The poetry may have changed, but the passion that won an empire can be seen in a pitch invasion at Millwall.

88

The difference is this, however: the territory to be subjugated now is not India or Quebec, but Luton or Leicester. And the enemy to be conquered is not the Spanish Armada or Napoleon's cavalry, but the West Ham casuals. And the great decisive battle? In San Marino.

89

Cantona embraces history. Should he, therefore, introduce the rawness and commitment of Tommy football into Europe? *Non!* That would be absurd. It is his destiny, rather, to bring a dab of European colour to England.

90

A theory of translation. The French for London is Paris. The English for Charles de Gaulle is Heathrow. The English for Racine is Shakespeare. The French for Ray Cooney is Molière.

91

The English for the Little Sparrow is Elaine Page. The French for Bournemouth is St Tropez. The English for Catherine Deneuve is Linda Lusardi.

92

The French for Vinny Jones, the lion-hearted ball winner, is Luc Frocard, Auxerre's midfield dynamo. The French for 'Psycho' Pearce, the barrel-thighed Forest defender, is Guy Le Cochon, the Belgian clogger.

93

The English for Gallic flair is to get stuck in where the boots are flying about.

94

What, then, is English for Cantona? Is Cantona untranslatable?

95

Evidemment. The English for Cantona is . . . Cantona!

96

Away to Paris Saint-Germain. The usual searching questions for the home team's defence.

97

'Here's one, Gaston. Was Mozart a conduit through whom God spoke to the world?'

98

'Faire quoi?'

99

Nul un!

100

Another victory – and afterwards the now familiar sense of *ennui*. Every achievement is a servitude. It compels us to a higher sense of achievement.

101

After the game, Cantona strolls along the Left Bank, pondering the new challenge: the Premiership!

102

Outside Les Deux Magots, philosophy students are deconstructing *Que signifie Gazza? Les pensées d'un idiot savant* (Gallimard, 1990). Cantona's football skills are not in doubt, but can he compete with England's most lucid contemporary poet of disillusion – and with his ever-present Boswell, M. Cinq Estomacs?

103

Cantona pauses. He joins the debate; he reads out an extract from *Que signifie Gazza?* '*Quand Sheryl m'a dit que je serais un papa, j'ai chié mes pantalons.*' It would sound better in English, of course.

104

When a poem is translated from one language into another it is the poetry which gets left out.

105

France's intellectual debt to England. Benny Hill. Norman Wisdom, Commander of *La Légion d'honneur français.* Max Wall, revered by Beckett. Hitchcock, the master of elegant suspense. *Continuez à monter le Khyber*, a seminal influence on Jean-Luc Godard. J.B. Priestley. C.P. Snow. Roger Scruton. *Myths and Memories* by Gilbert Adair.

106

There is a saying in France: 'Where Barthes obscured, Adair enlightens.' The aphorisms of Adam Phillips and their mysterious aplomb.

107

London's celebrated café life, where the graceful boulevards throb with talk. 'How madly riveting!' 'What's your news? Do tell!' 'You don't say!' An abstract idea is posed alfresco in Sloane Square. It is doused immediately before it can catch fire. It flickers briefly at the Beaufort Street traffic lights, but is finally put out in Finsborough Road before it can become an arid 'ism'.

108

England! Land of contrasts, of mystery and romance – and *la vie en gris*. Trafalgar Square. Le pop. Hotpants. Vivienne Westwood. 'Closed till Thursday.' Traitors' Gate. Sid Vicious. Madam Speaker. The Smurfs. *Ready Steady Cook!* Le Tea Dance. Thick crombies over old-time dancing gowns in Piccadilly. Middle-aged women cycling to Communion through the mist. Lengthening shadows on a county ground. Cocoa. Nanny. Six of the best. 'Weeee'll meet agaaaaaiin . . .'

109

Shaftesbury Avenue. The natural setting for the world's leading actors and their intimidating diction. The conch and codpiece. 'Once more unto the breach, dear friends, once more . . .'

110

Haiku 2
'Pauline Quirk. Me Lords
Dance and Hopkins. Stratford Johns.
They'll do for me, John.'

111

Soho! Home of *la vie en gris*. Crowded pubs, prawns in the basket. Stern injunctions. 'Last orders!' 'No smoking!' 'No loitering!' Paul Raymond's internationally renowned Revuebar, where men with naval binoculars sit alone in cubicles.

112

Here is the very heart of *la vie en gris*. Slung up in the traction of his inhibitions, the Englishman in his cubicle is yet freer than the skipping Frenchman.

113

A sudden memory. Cantona is eight years old. He cannot sleep. Downstairs, old men discuss *la vie en gris* in a smoke-filled room. His father, his grandfather, three gnarled seniors from the village pull deeply on their pipes. Cantona climbs out of bed. He pauses on the stairs, listens to the conversation. The old men talk nostalgically of times past when it was customary for fathers to take their sons to Soho *pour* – the old men lower their voices – *perdre leurs cerises*.

114

The old men lower their voices still further.
The boy Cantona strains his ears to catch
their words. *'Un cabaret et, après, un
"dangerous liaison" avec* Madam Stern *à*
Greek Street.'

115

Forbidden fruit tastes sweetest. The
Englishman understands that the sharpest
pleasures must have an edge of shame.

116

Truly, *le vice français* is a limiting disregard
for seemly inhibition.

117

Small wonder that '*un* dangerous liaison' has
entered the French language along with '*le*
picnic', 'I regret nothing', '*le* more things
change, the more they are the same', '*le*
sixty-nine' and '*les* English lessons – third
floor'.

118

So – will Cantona accept the invitation to
play the beautiful game in Leeds?

119

Leeds? What does it signify? Knobby faces,
kippers for tea, frozen stone-blasters high on
scaffolding, urchins playing in the street.
Fog, sodium lights, false teeth. Large fighting
women with rolling pins.

120

Each night, when he goes to bed, Cantona
dreams of Leeds. Flat caps. Whippets.
S. Bucket & Son, General Provisioners.
Twine. Nails. Oxo cubes. The *Sporting Life*.
Woodbines. Boiled sweets in a jar. A sense of
community.

121

'Can't complain.'
'This overcoat will see me out.'
'There'll be a shortage of toilet rolls by
Christmas, I read it in the *Daily Mirror*.'

122

The mayor in a waistcoat on a podium. A works band from the foundry. Muck and brass. 'Nowt's for nowt, lad. Remember that.'

123

Billy Bremner. Big Jack. Terry Cooper. Trevor Cherry.

124

The famous old-time music hall. The City of Varieties. 'Can you hear me, mother?'

125

Norman 'Bite Yer Legs' Hunter!

126

If the silkworm is an even deeper expression of what is Chinese than the ideographic script, what is the deepest expression of what is English? London? Stringfellow's? Stocks-in-Town? White Hart Lane? Highbury? Stamford Bridge?

127

Non! Leeds. Leeds is *authentic* England. To be kicked into the north stand of a wet Saturday afternoon by Norman 'Bite Yer Legs' Hunter is the most authentic experience of England that a visitor can have.

128

What of Chelsea? Chelsea is a club for tourists and Italians. For haircuts and cat-walk players. For ladies who lunch and Harvey Nichols. For perms and preening, on and off the ball. For celebrities, not heroes.

129

On the day that Harvey Nichols opens a branch in Leeds, Leeds will not be Leeds.

130

Soon enough the sugar of celebrity will turn to vinegar; and nowhere quicker than in a capital city.

131

Cantona is enjoying a cognac in a local *tabac*. 'Chelsea? Playboys!' he says. 'Ask Alan Hudson! Ask Peter Osgood!'

'Who?' says the barman.

'Précisément.'

'Pour être juste, Eric, what about Besty – the king of the playboys? He didn't play for Chelsea,' says the barman.

'Encore un cognac, s'il vous plaît.'

132

The hero creates himself; the celebrity is
created by the media. The hero is a big man;
the celebrity is a big name.

133

The can of soup? The face of Monroe?
Which is the celebrity?

134

The soft south and champagne football.
Bubbles and hiccups. In the north they give
it some welly. Cantona will go north and get
stuck in. He'll be an authentic hero.

135

His telegram to Wilko of Leeds says it all:
'The salmon that idles its way downstream
will never leap the waterfall.'

136

Donc.

137
Leeds!

138
The haikus continue to flow.

Haiku 3
'England. Mushy peas
Jam butties and warm lager.
You can't whack it, John.'

139
Cantona's final game in France. A friendly at
home to Belgium. He is marked by Guy Le
Cochon, the Belgian clogger. Studs, elbows,
scything tackles. When Le Cochon has the
ball he is uncomfortable with it. He is in a
bad marriage with it. He wants it to go away
from him. He wants to kick it very hard. For
Le Cochon a kick is not a kick. It is an
expression of dysfunctionality.

140

France have a corner. There is jostling and banter in the box. Cantona's decision to play the beautiful game in England is common knowledge now. One of the French players mentions the language problem. The Belgian clogger gets in his retaliation first. 'What language problem?' he scoffs. 'The English can speak it. How hard can it be?'

141

Only in Belgium are the English seen as gormless buffoons. Each Christmas an idiotic collection of jokes, *Les Blagues anglaises*, tops the bestseller lists in Brussels.

142

Should Socrates have complained had a donkey kicked him? Cantona lets his football do the talking. He feints to the left, swerves to the right and volleys the ball past the Belgian keeper.

143
Un nul!

144

The game continues. Le Cochon, the Belgian clogger, lunges at Cantona with his studs showing. 'Did you hear about the Englishman who won the Tour de France and did a lap of honour?'

145

Cantona ripostes with his educated left foot. He slots the ball between the Belgian clogger's legs and glides easily away.

146

The Belgian clogger comes panting and gasping in pursuit. 'Did you hear about the English striker who missed a penalty? The goalkeeper sent him the wrong way.' In desperation Le Cochon sticks out a foot and trips Cantona in the box. Penalty! Cantona strolls up to take it himself.

147

Deux nul!

148

The Belgian clogger hasn't had enough. 'Did you hear about the Englishman who was up for indecent assault? At the identity parade he stepped forward and said: "She's the one!"'

149

The final whistle. Cantona rejoices that henceforth he will play the beautiful game in the home of *le* fair play, a land where bigotry is unknown.

150

The day of his departure draws near. He prepares himself. He buys a phrase-book. He learns to say 'The pen of my aunt.' 'Excuse me, sir, my husband has a stomach upset.' 'Does that include the full English breakfast?' He throws the book away. In England, of course, the phrase-books will be more sophisticated. He'll buy one there.

151

He decides, however, that he will be driven
to England from his home in Provence,
gaining knowledge on the way. He equips
himself with Arthur Eperon's *L'Angleterre
inconnue* – with its celebrated introduction
by Frank and Nesta Bough.

152

'This indispensable book,' as Frank and
Nesta say in their introduction, 'gives us a
tantalising glimpse under the petticoats of
L'Angleterre inconnue, suggesting hidden
delights that, astonishingly, French
holidaymakers never knew existed.'

153

Mr Eperon offers a choice of six routes
through authentic England – each avoiding
the well-beaten tourist tracks – of which two
particularly appeal to Cantona: *la route en
gris* and *la route en bleu*.

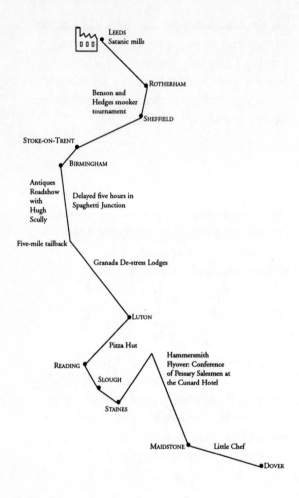

LEEDS
Satanic mills

ROTHERHAM

Benson and
Hedges snooker
tournament

SHEFFIELD

STOKE-ON-TRENT

BIRMINGHAM

Antiques
Roadshow
with
Hugh
Scully

Delayed five hours in
Spaghetti Junction

Five-mile tailback

Granada De-stress Lodges

LUTON

Pizza Hut

Hammersmith
Flyover: Conference
of Pessary Salesmen at
the Cunard Hotel

READING

SLOUGH

STAINES

MAIDSTONE   Little Chef

DOVER

Route 1
La route en gris –
a journey through
England at work

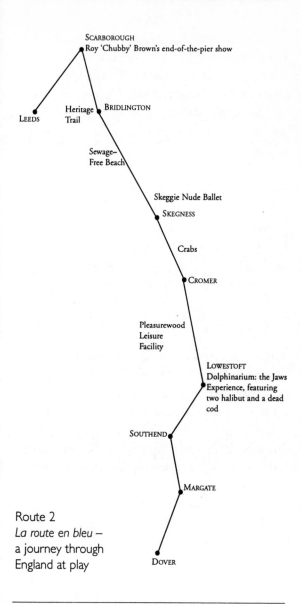

SCARBOROUGH
Roy 'Chubby' Brown's end-of-the-pier show

Heritage   BRIDLINGTON
Trail

LEEDS

Sewage–
Free Beach

Skeggie Nude Ballet

SKEGNESS

Crabs

CROMER

Pleasurewood
Leisure
Facility

LOWESTOFT
Dolphinarium: the Jaws
Experience, featuring
two halibut and a dead
cod

SOUTHEND

MARGATE

DOVER

Route 2
La route en bleu –
a journey through
England at play

154

After careful thought, Cantona chooses
Route 1, *la route en gris*. He is not, after all,
visiting England *en vacances* – though a
night at the Cunard Hotel, Hammersmith,
will break the journey nicely. There will be
plenty of time to explore seaside England at
a later date.

155

His possessions are packed, the car loaded.
He travels in the back. He sleeps, he dreams
of England – images from television
programmes and from perusing *Country Life*.

156

The car purrs northwards. Would the
English still wear bowler hats if they knew
that they had been designed originally for
Herr Hans Bowler, a Bavarian businessman
whose head was shaped like a traffic cone?
Possibly. They still play cricket – invented in
Italy in 1785 – and where are the Elgin
Marbles? Where is Cleopatra's Needle?
Where is the Stone of Scone? It is one of the
Englishman's greatest strengths that he can
appropriate the foreign and believe that it is
immeasurably improved.

157

And yet – who is the thief? The courtesan who proudly wears a diamond ring? Or the magpie who takes it from her dressing-table?

158

The car glides through France. Cantona dreams of England. Tea and toast. Curates. Thin legs. Pale women with sunburnt knees. Panama hats. 'Bottoms up!' 'Pip pip!' 'Gorblimey, guv!'

159

He wakes up. He hears voices.
'Your turn to take the kids to school, Veronica!'
'Right you are, Vernon!'
He looks around. A man in shorts reads the *Daily Telegraph*. A woman in a hat makes cucumber sandwiches under an apple tree. A group of children absorbed in a game of cricket. 'I'm Gower!' cries one. 'I'm Botham!' cries another.

160

Cantona speaks. 'We've arrived! It's just as I expected!' His chauffeur replies. 'I'm afraid not, Eric. You dozed off. We're still in Provence.'

161

Leeds at last! A press reception at Elland Road, organised by Wilko. A clamour of voices in a foreign tongue. An interpreter steps forward. Cantona waves him away. His theory of translation will suffice. He understands the international language of the tabloid press. The English for *Ici Paris* is the *Northern Echo*. The French for John Motson is Jean Le Rodent. He takes the first question in his stride.

162

'Eric, many skilful little Continentals have tried to make their mark in the Premiership, but we have a saying here: tackle a Frenchman hard and his bottle goes. What makes you think you can succeed where so many have failed?'

163

Cantona replies. 'In France we too have a saying: when the rutting caribou mounts – '

164

'THANK you, gentlemen!' Wilko intervenes. 'That will be all for now.' The press are sent away. The reception is over.

165

A discussion with Wilko about Cantona's place in the Leeds line-up. Cantona assumes the formation on the park will be 4–3–3, as in the glory days. In goal, Gary Sprake, the fallible Welshman. Paul Reaney at right back; at left back, Terry Cooper. The centre backs, Big Jack and Norman 'Bite yer Legs' Hunter. In midfield, Johnny Giles, Billy Bremner and Trevor Cherry. Up front, the big lad Jones, 'Sniffer' Clark and Peter Lorimer who, according to Motty, 'literally had dynamite in both boots'.

166

Wilko shakes his head. 'No, no. We've changed all that.'

167

Cantona is impressed. He is able to translate Wilko's saying into French. *'Nous avons changé tout cela.' Non.* It sounded better in English.

168

He discovers that the present formation is 4–4–1. He will play in the hole behind Lee Chapman, the big striker, running into space and picking the ball up from Gordon Strachan, the little midfield dynamo from Scotland.

169

Haiku 4
'Eric the jockey
The big lad, Chapman, as the
Horse. Nice one, Wilko!'

170

The psychology of positions on the pitch. If character is more often expressed through choice than through words or even actions, what could be more revealing of personality than choice of position on the field of play?

171

So – what is a winger telling the world about himself?

172

He is involved in the game, yet not involved. At best, he is a gadfly stinging the flesh of the opposition. At worst, he might as well be sipping from a thermos flask in the back row of the stands for all the part he plays. The essential outsider of the beautiful game, the winger will never be short of acquaintances, yet he will forever remain a stranger, even to himself.

173

On the pitch he is Giggsy, Ginola,
McManaman, Pat Nevin, the wee Scottish
Marxist. Off the pitch, Lewis Carroll,
Howard Hodgkin, Miranda Richardson,
J.P. Donleavy, Rik Mayall, Jane Birkin,
Jerry Hayes.

174

Wilko is concerned that Cantona may be
lonely in his new surroundings. He suggests
that he keeps a cat for company. Cantona
declines. 'I have my neighbours.' Wilko is
not convinced. 'But they can't speak French.'
Cantona ponders for a moment. 'Can the
cat?'

175

The true manager and the champagne manager. Which is Wilko? Certainly his clothes, his reticence, his general air of thoughtfulness, suggest a man more interested in soccer than soundbites, a man who finds more eloquence in boot and ball than in mere words.

176

And yet. Within days of Cantona's arrival, Wilko seems to have changed. Seeing the Frenchman reading Michel Tournier's *Le Roi des Aulnes*, he reveals that he has written a racy football novel, called *The Stud*.

177

As Cantona politely discusses Lacan's theory of metafictional irony, Wilko becomes more and more animated.

178

There is a change in his team-talks, too.
Asked whether Blackburn's super-striker
should be marked, he shrugs.

179

*'Que sais-je? En fin de compte, c'est le destin
qui marque l'homme.'*

180

'You what, gaffer?' asks Strachany, the wee
Scottish ginger-nut.

181

'L'état, c'est moi,' says Wilko.

182

Cantona scratches his head. It would sound better in English, no doubt.

183

He decides to buy himself an English phrase-book. He learns to translate '*La plume de ma tante.*' '*Excusez-moi, monsieur, mais mon mari a mal au ventre.*' '*Est-ce que le petit déjeuner anglais est inclus?*' He is disappointed. He had expected better from an English phrase-book. He throws it away. He decides to compile his own phrase-book. He will listen and learn. He will familiarise himself with the language and culture of his new home town. He approaches a young police officer in the street. 'Excuse me, officer, but which of your opera houses is the best?'

184

'Here! Are you taking the fucking piss or what?'

185

Cantona makes the first entry in his phrase-book. 'Cheery responses in the street . . .'

186

In at the deep end. Away to Wimbledon. Intimidating graffiti on the walls of the visitors' dressing-room. Deafening rap music plays through the intercom. The game itself is a war of juddering contact, of mud and studs, of route one, of up and under and verbal abuse.

187

Fair enough, Brian. The English understand that the feelings induced by football must be of a kind the multitudes can share. English football must not, therefore, depend on the innovative or complex. It must derive from the basic images ordinary people have engraved on their memories: the school bully confounded by the weed, the absent father, first love, brotherhood, our kid, the motherland betrayed, an unmarked grave in a distant land.

188

Cantona tells himself that this is the destiny of the true artist: not to compose exquisitely in an ivory tower, but to dirty himself in a dark, repulsive universe of pain. Wimbledon.

189

By his uncompromising commitment, he
has won the respect of Wilko and the lads.

190

A poet is a barometer, but he is also part of
the weather.

191

On the team coach going back to Leeds,
there is camaraderie and banter. Cantona is
included. He is accepted now as one of the
lads.

192

''Ere, Eric. Is it true that you lot invented
soixante-neuf, then?'

193

Cantona considers. At last he speaks. 'Who can judge the beauty of the diving cormorant more perfectly than the very herring it consumes?'

194

'Yeah, right. Fair enough, Eric.'

195

In France, the name Eric, like Albert and Ernest, indicates a lofty, middle-class intellectualism. As *un philosophe du parc*, as a people's poet, Cantona had rejected it. *'Moi? Je suis Cantona!'* In England, he has already discovered that the name is associated with beer-swilling darts players, with broad comedians and beauty contest entrepreneurs. For the first time in his life, he is at ease with his given name.

196

The team coach speeds north to Leeds.
Cantona chuckles to himself.

197

'Moi? Je suis Eric!'

198

The poet, the artist, the heroic actor, the
great sportsman? Each is two people: the
performer – the creator of beautiful fictions
– and *himself.*

199

The great artist: 'As *myself* I could not do or
say these things.'

200

The great artist transcends himself.

201

Dame Ninette de Valois? Margot Fonteyn?
John Wayne? Pele? As Edith Stannus, the
doctor's wife from Sunningdale, as little
Peggy Hookham from Staines, as Marion
Morrison from Wisconsin, as Edson Arantes
de Nascimento, heading a coconut on the
beaches of Brazil, could they have worked
their magic on stage, screen and playing-
field?

202

Cantona has made a contribution to the
philosophy of identity. 'I am Eric. But on an
open stage I weave my fantasies as Cantona!'

203

What, then, is Cantona? Cantona is an
imaginative construct, a collaboration
between himself, the media and the fans. A
journalist, a fan, an opposing player – they
meet only Cantona, and, when sharing a
stage with him, are participating in a drama.
But Eric is private – known only to himself,
his loved ones and the lads.

204

Eric is *authentic*. Cantona is created.
Existence precedes essence. Therein lies our
freedom.

205

No disrespect to the boss and to the other
lads on the coach, but they remain
uninvented. Their names say it all: Wilko.
Batto. Chappo. Dorigoey. Strachany.

206

'*Moi? Je suis* Wilko!'
'*Moi? Je suis* Batto!'
'*Moi? Je suis* Dorigoey!'
Non! We could only shake our heads and
look away.

207

And Gazza? Gazza is a puzzle. Adored in
Italy and, as the *idiot savant*, endlessly
deconstructed on Paris's Left Bank, he
remains obstinately uncompleted. He has
none of the awesome unity of the great
artist. Whatever 'Gazza' is, it remains
uninvented, on and off the field.

208

The poet is in command of his fantasy, while it is exactly the mark of the neurotic, the eternal adolescent (Danny Baker, Paula Yates, Jerry Hayes), that he is possessed by his fantasy.

209

That said, one can't help feeling some affection for the *idiot savant*, whose name, interestingly enough, means 'I have suffered' in Icelandic.

210

Gazza has it in him to play the great parts, but can he *imagine* himself to greatness?

211

The celebrated theatrical scandal which rocked London in 1951. Gielgud's Richard II at the Old Vic. Robert Newton, who had it in him to be the finest actor of his generation, enters as John of Gaunt. The audience holds its breath. Here is greatness.

212

'If you think I'm pissed, wait till you see the Duke of Buckingham.'

213

Newton was the Gazza of his day. Genius imposes obligations which he declined to shoulder. Will Gazza learn?

214

You cannot step into the same river twice. And yet. To define yourself is ultimately like trying to lick your own tongue.

215

The English sense of humour. The lads are watching television in the saloon bar of the Goat in Boots.

216

The presenter introduces a documentary.
'This week, we will bring you up to date
with the evil men exposed in previous
programmes. Stalkers. Kidnappers. Drug
fiends. Foreign fishermen.'

217

Cantona chuckles. This is a joke – refutation
of the slander current in Europe that the
English, unlike the French and the Germans,
are unable to laugh at themselves. He turns
to the lads. 'Get out of that! Rock on,
Tommy! Can you hear me, mother?'

218

The lads aren't laughing. It hadn't been a
joke. Cantona is embarrassed by his mistake.
Self-mockery, like charm, is an act of
ingratiation and submission. The French and
Germans, by laughing at themselves, are
saying: 'Your dad's bigger than my dad.' The
English are above such things. He still has
much to learn.

219

The psychology of positions on the pitch.
The midfielder is the party host who fades
into the background when the speech of
thanks is made. He is the office manager
who does all the work and yet is the first to
congratulate the less talented on his
promotion.

220

Ill at ease with his own success, the
midfielder is a facilitator, an enabler, with a
strong sense of family. Many nurses are
midfielders.

221

On the pitch, he is Strachany, Batto, Robbo,
Wisey. Off the pitch, he is Vanessa Redgrave,
Umberto Eco, Dr Johnson, Shirley Williams,
Tim Rice, Mark Knopfler, Saatchi and
Saatchi.

222

Cantona listens to the radio. Jan Molby, the big Liverpool playmaker, is being interviewed.
'Tell me, Jan. What was your biggest difficulty settling in?'
'The language problem, John.'
'The lads couldn't speak Danish?'
'No, John. They couldn't speak English.'

223

Motty has said of Cantona: 'His mother tongue is French, but he can make the ball speak in any language.'

224

True. He decides, however, to take English lessons from the Danish playmaker.

225

The eloquent snow goose travels further than the mute swan.

226

Cantona prepares himself for his first lesson
with the big playmaker. He listens and
learns. He has discovered that there are two
sorts of English: 1. Incorrect, or colloquial,
as used by the lads, and current in pubs and
on the street. 2. Correct, as heard on the
BBC. He makes many entries in his phrase-
book.

227

Colloquial: Sorted. Not half. Well iffy. You
looking at my bird, Jimmy? Not many. Awa'
the lads. Half fancy. Diamond. Geezer.
Double hard bastard. She's a sort, that. She's
the dog's bollocks. Whaddyermean you'd
rather cop a handful of Rachel's
thingimmies? I'll blurra poot ma boot up yer
. . . You taking the piss, or what? That
Gullit's a boss player, innit.

228

Correct, BBC: 'To be fair, Brian.' 'At the end
of the day, Brian.' 'He'll do for me, Brian.'
'He'll be disappointed not to have got on the
end of that one, Brian.' 'We'd all like some
of that, Brian.'

229

Away to Liverpool. The talk at half-time is
all about a spindly-legged lad with blinding
pace and skill on the ball. Wilko sums up
the thinking in the Leeds dressing-room.
'The lad, McManamany. He could be the
new Tom Finney.'

230

Cantona is silent. There comes into his mind
the image of a small, gnarled man in a pork-
pie hat. Combative, Scottish, unintelligible –
once, in his presence, a reporter had said of a
new lad that he played like Tom Finney. The
grizzled senior had thought for a while. At
last he'd spoken:

231

'Aye. So he does. But remember this – Tom's
65.'

232

That had been Shanks. For 30 years Shanks
had had a love affair with the Kop. Shanks
had seen it all before. Shanks was a gaffer.
And Wilko?

233

After the game, Cantona has his first English lesson from the big Danish playmaker. Cantona has been practising. "'Ere, ponce orf innit Jan, she's gorra birraformoner.' The big playmaker scratches his head. He cannot understand.

234

Cantona tries again. He speaks correct, BBC, English. He lays out his stall. He turns on a sixpence. He finishes clinically. He's so sharp in the box he could shave himself. The first yard's in his mind. The big playmaker still can't understand.

235

Cantona makes a last attempt. He speaks in his own language.

236

'The whale may not be a fish. But nor is the red herring.'

237

The big playmaker shakes his head. The lessons are discontinued.

238

Cantona is settling in. 'Switch it.' 'One-two.' 'Push up.' 'Have a word, ref.' Is there any sweeter symphony than the constant communication between the 23 players on the park during an English game? In comparison, the European game is played in a rapt silence of concentration. The onanistic concentration of solitary exhibitionists.

239

A theory of passion. If passion is P, skill is S, vulnerability is V, commitment is C and well-gutted is W, then the English game can be expressed as:

$$P^2 + \sqrt{(C + V)} - S^3 = W$$

240

The paradox of passion. The Italian Serie A
is cool and defensive. The French League is a
graveyard made gaudy by individual displays
of hot-house orchids. The Bundesliga is
courteous and tactical. Only in the
Premiership is the full theatre of human
experience expressed on the park.

241

Kitsch and English football. In England it is
regarded as a sign of strength to cry. After a
rare defeat away to Coventry, Cantona is
surprised to discover that he alone is dry-
eyed. In a dressing-room awash with tears,
even the reticent Wilko is hunched over in
grief.

242

Haiku 5
'Tessa Sanderson,
Gazza in bits. Paul Merson.
I love this country!'

243

In England no man is flattered to his face.
This is why Englishmen keep dogs. It is
permissible to flatter a man on the score of
his dog's excellence.

244

Cantona meets Lord Winterburn, a Leeds
supporter, at his home. The butler brings in
tea and cucumber sandwiches. He is
accompanied by Lord Winterburn's labrador,
Archie. The labrador is introduced. But not
the butler.

245

Lady Winterburn enters. 'What in the name
of arse is going on?' Cantona is introduced.
Lady Winterburn asks him what he does.
'I'm a professional footballer.'
'That will keep you busy.' She turns away
and talks to Archie, the labrador. Cantona is
impressed.

246

Later, he makes two entries in his phrase-book. 'Examples of English economical politeness: "That will keep you busy." "What in the name of arse is going on?"'

247

That night, Cantona has an unusual dream. It is the Cup final at Wembley. Leeds win! He climbs the steps to the Royal Box. He is presented with his medal.
'Congratulations, M. Cantona.'
'Thank you, ma'am. And what do you do?'
'I'm the Queen.'
'That will keep you busy.'
Bien.

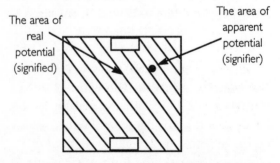

A player's greatest challenge is not the ball but the space around the ball. His best moves involve feints, dummies and running into space. A truly great artist of the beautiful game can be man of the match without once touching the ball.

248

Cantona greatly admires the Queen. The coronation of a monarch is as much the validation of a collective fantasy as the confirmation of a *de facto* role. The Queen is at one and the same time fact and fiction. She is as real in her way as Bet Lynch or Inspector Maigret. She is the apotheosis of performance art. Her grip on the fantasy never loosens.

249

It is England's misfortune that some of the younger members of the Royal Family – in their refusal (paradoxically, an essentially Continental refusal) to sustain the fiction – seem to have taken Gazza, the *idiot savant*, as their role model rather than Cantona.

250

That said, the greatest artists must sometimes fail. This is their privilege. In the theatre, the supporting actor (Herbert Lom) returns the same performance night after night. On the park, the supporting player (Batto) can achieve a level of consistency denied to the heroic player. The heroic actor must dare to fail.

251

The great actor will interpret his role
according to the circumstances.

252

Away to Wimbledon? At home to AC
Milan? They are different dramas. One is a
farce by Ray Cooney. The other a tragedy by
Racine. To deliver the same performance
would be an act of bad taste. To rise to some
occasions is inappropriate. The true artist
must dare to disappoint. The supporting
actor never disappoints. Away to
Wimbledon, at home to AC Milan –
whatever the drama, Chappo and Batto,
Strachany and Dorigoey, never vary their
performances. This is how it should be.

253

A mystery, however. In England, where
spear-carriers – Bally, Belly, Nobby, Bully,
Batty – have always been adored, Cantona is
treated as a hero. Why is this? Because he
gets stuck in when the boots are flying?
Perhaps so.

'Push up!'

'Flick it to Chappo!'

'Give and go!'

'One-two!'

'See you down Scribes West!'

The Champagne Manager's
half-time team-talk

'Yir oot ay order, laddie'

'Shut yir fookin' mooth'

'You want a fookin' burst
mooth, coont?'

'Dinnae fookin' start, laddie'

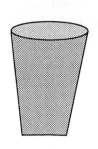

The Gaffer's half-time team-talk

254

A theory of life. Each person is born either a referee or a player.

255

But how many are referees masquerading as players? How many players would be more comfortable running backwards, blowing a whistle, reaching for a red or yellow card at moments of crisis?

256

What is a referee? He is a person who likes to study and judge his fellow man. She is one whose reactions are based on training rather than instinct.

257

They run backwards, they wave their arms, they cry 'Play on!' to life – but they remain at one remove from its passion and danger. That is their privilege, and their tragedy.

258

Tony Blair? A referee.
John Prescott? A player.
Joanna Lumley? A referee.
Helena Bonham-Carter? A player.
Saint? A referee.
Greavesie? A prat.

259

And history's most eminent referee? Tom
Paine, whose declaration of *The Rights of
Man* provides the ultimate rule-book for the
great game.

260

However. As Baudelaire pointed out, Paine
omitted two rights: the right to contradict
oneself and the right to leave.

261

Here we see the difference between the
referee and the player, the citizen and the
artist.

262

For the player/artist, the greatest freedom is the freedom of the soul. The referee/citizen is different: his strength lies in the very limit of his vision.

263

The player/artist is Samuel Beckett, Pablo Picasso, Percy Bysshe Shelley, Coco Chanel, Raymond Carver, Eric Cantona. And the referee/citizen? Victor Hugo, Thomas Gainsborough, T.S. Eliot, Kenneth Branagh, André Malraux, Penelope Lively, Gary Mabbutt.

264

For the referee, it is inconceivable to end a sentence with a question mark. To ask a question is to open the door to an avalanche of answers, disputes and further questions, to all of which the referee will raise a red card, tremblingly pronouncing it 'dissent'.

265

For the true player, all meaningful sentences must end in a question mark. He will not say, 'You must be fucking joking, ref,' but rather, 'If one were to deconstruct the recommended course of action, might one not reveal its flawed logic, ref?'

266

For the referee, the final whistle provides a sense of clearly defined closure. For the player, it is but a temporary pause in the one game that matters – the great inner game of life.

267

Cantona's first recorded word? *'Pourquoi?'*

268

Who's the wanker? Who's the wanker? Who's the wanker in the black? We do not know. To control the beautiful game and never to score a goal is a paradigm of self-abuse.

269

Lord Winterburn's labrador, Archie, dies. Cantona sends a note of condolence. 'We have a saying in France: "Soon enough a labrador must die." Not a particularly profound saying, but strangely appropriate on this occasion.'

270

Away to Notts Forest at the City Ground. Cantona meets Brian Clough. 'Listen, young man. A hippopotamus may not have a sting in its tail, but a wise man would rather be sat on by a wasp. You won't find that in the coaching manual.' Cantona understands. He responds. 'We have a saying up north. The wife can put your supper on the table, but is she as quick as a ferret down a rabbit hole? We're not daft in Leeds.'

271

He and Cloughie can communicate through
the deep grammar of a metalanguage. In
future, they will receive English lessons from
one another.

272

Pliny: 'One grows to love a country as soon
as one gets to know many ridiculous people
in it.'

273
Absolument!

274

Haiku 6
'Christopher Biggins.
Two fat cooks. Winner's Dinners.
I love this country!'

275

Cantona reflects upon the nature of management. Is there a difference between the champagne manager and the gaffer? The champagne manager is obsessed with general ideas learnt parrot-fashion: flat back four, overlapping wing backs, Christmas-tree formations.

276

The gaffer is interested only in specifics: this game, this player, this life.

277

The champagne manager prefers the commentary box to the dug-out, has ambitions only to be an 'expert summariser' for the TV big match.

278

The gaffer wants only to win the big match.

279

The champagne manager can deconstruct a game instantly. 'He'll have to hold up his hand for that one.' 'He can do that for fun.' 'It's just another day at the office for United's defence.' 'Maldini? That's spelt C–L–A–S–S in any language.'

280

The gaffer says it all with a cold glance and an indecipherable growl.

281

The champagne manager has an FA coaching certificate. The gaffer has a degree in people from the University of Real Life.

282

The champagne manager thinks like a headline in the *Sun*. The gaffer doesn't think at all. He is above thinking. He feels.

283
Which, then, is Wilko? Cantona reserves judgement.

284
So – if A is an Armani suit, M is a gold medallion, P is a post-match soundbite, S is membership of Stringfellow's and R is 'the season's gone pear-shaped on us', the champagne manager can be expressed as:

$$A^3 + (M + P)^2 + S = R$$

285
If I is inarticulate, S is Scottish, H is a '40s haircut, W is a demob suit and D is the double, then a gaffer's season can be expressed by the equation:

$$\frac{I^2}{S} + (H + W) = D$$

286

At home to Notts Forest. Cantona and
Cloughie discuss the language problem.
Cloughie speaks: 'Listen, young man. I've
been visiting foreign parts for 27 years, and
they still can't understand me. Once in a
supermarket I wanted some eggs. I flapped
my arms and went "cluck, cluck". They gave
me toilet rolls.'
Cantona understands. 'Was that in
Marbella?'
'No, young man. It were in West Ham in
'88.'

287

Cantona can now speak English better than
Brian Clough. But he continues to make
entries in his phrase-book.

288

'For me, Atko, the little Nigerians, for all
their silky skills up front, are very naïve at
the back.'

289

He has learnt that in correct, BBC, English,
'naïve' means black.

290

From the BBC he also learns that 'crude'
means Turkish.
'I'm afraid the heroic English middleweight
has no answer to the crude slugger from
Turkey.'
'You ain't wrong, 'Arry. Oh my good God.
There 'e goes now.'
'Still, he put up a brave fight, Frank.'
'So 'e did, 'Arry. Oh good God. There 'e
goes again.'

291

Cantona listens and learns. 'Cynical' means
Italian. 'Arrogant' means German. 'Excitable'
means French. 'Unruly' means Spanish.

292

Are his beloved English racist, then?
Consider. A tall man scores goals. Fools
mock the way his hair is cut. A television
comedian says it looks as if he has a
pineapple on his head. The tall man hears
the laughter. He becomes embarrassed. He
stops scoring goals. At the end of the day,
who is the fool? Who the pineapple?

293

Cantona discusses the matter with Brian
Clough. 'Racist, young man? Not at Notts
Forest, we're not. A lad can be white, black,
blue, pink, brown. He can be purple with
yellow spots. That's his prerogative. Just as
long as he sticks the ball in the back of the
net come 3 p.m. of a Saturday afternoon
he'll be all right with me. Otherwise he'll be
back up a banana tree. We're not stupid at
Notts Forest.'

294

Haiku 6
'Trevor Macdonald.
Frank Bruno. Moira Stewart.
They'll do for me, John.'

295

The psychology of positions on the pitch.
For the striker, his own success means more
than that of the team. He lives for the
plaudits, claps his hands above his head in
response to any chant containing his name.
He is never happier than when being
embraced by his team-mates after he has
scored a goal. His sense of self makes him
strong, brave, happy to dive in where the
boots are flying about. But when the crowd
has gone home, no one is more alone.

296

On the pitch, Zico, Baggio, Greavesie,
Sparky Hughes, Klinsmann, Chappo,
Maradona, Sniffer Clarke. Off the pitch,
Sartre, Brando, Madonna, Will Self, Liam
Gallagher, Rick Stein, Amanda de Cadenet.

297

The artist and the media. Has an artist an obligation to explain himself, to trivialise the art he serves by promoting it on a television panel game? Did Beckett, wearing a brightly coloured V-necked sweater, participate in *'Pardonnez-vous mes culottes! Une compilation hilare des grands accidents du théâtre'*?

298

'What was your most embarrassing moment, M. Beckett?'

299

'Well, Pierre, on the opening night of *Waiting for Godot* in Paris, there was some restlessness in the audience during the longer silences. Suddenly, a bell accidentally rang backstage. "Whoever it is, for God's sake let him in!" cried a member of the audience. We had to laugh!'

300

'That's truly remarkable, M. Beckett!'

301

Non! It is not imaginable.

302

Cantona is invited to appear on *A Question of Sport* – a TV panel game in which sporting 'personalities' vie with one another to trivialise their chosen discipline. 'What happened next?' 'Spot the sporting bloomer!' It is less vulgar, perhaps, than French TV's current disgrace, *Ils pensent que c'est tout au dessus,* but the beautiful game should not be mocked with facetious clips and giggling out-takes.

303

Travelling home on the team coach after a trip to Highbury, Wilko urges Cantona to take part – for the good of the club – but Cantona declines. Does he think he's bigger than the club? *Non!*

304

'When the chess pieces are put back in the box, the king is no mightier than the humble pawn.'

305

However. The game is bigger than the club.

306

A discussion develops about the philosophy of social objects. Cantona speaks. 'What can be predicated of a social object – a country, a debating society, a football club – cannot necessarily be predicated of its constituent parts.'

307

Wilko speaks. 'It's only a panel game, Eric.'

308

Cantona continues. 'For example, Glasgow is bigger than Stockholm but the average Scot is smaller than the large Swede.'

309

Strachany, the wee carrot-topped Scot, looks up from his game of cards. 'You having a go, Eric?'

310

Cantona develops the argument. 'So – can a social object be said to exist? Pierre points to a collection of trees. "Look at that forest," he says to his good friend, Henri. The next day, the trees are cut down. They are left lying on the ground. Does the forest still exist?'

311

'Point taken, Eric. You finished with the *Sun*, Batto?'

312

Cantona continues. 'Consider Leeds United Football Club. Is it greater than the sum of its parts? Imagine this. Its stadium is pulled down. Its players are sold to other clubs. Its fans change their allegiance to Sheffield Wednesday. Does Leeds United still exist?'

313

'Does Leedsness – square ball, push up, one-two, back in numbers, flick it to Eric – in some sense live on? I think not. A club is no more than the sum of its parts. But the beautiful game exists in heaven. The game is bigger than the club. *C'est tout.*'

314

Wilko speaks. 'Can I take that as a "no" to *A Question of Sport* then, Eric?'

315

Cantona's reply says it all. 'When the snow tiger does the charleston with the questing vole, each looks as ridiculous as the other.'

316

Linguistics. Cantona is explaining to Wilko the differing constructions in French of *avoir*, 'to have', and *être*, 'to be'. He asks the manager which of them he considers to be the essential footballing verb.

317

'At the end of the day, Eric, it's got to be "have". The game's all about possession. If you don't have the ball, you can't score. Rule one in the coaching manual, *n'est-ce pas?*'

318

'*Non.* On the park it is better to be at one with the ball than to have it. On the other hand, it is better to have character than to be a character. I conclude that Being and Having exist in perfect symbiosis, like the busy honey-bee pollinating the humble chrysanthemum.'

319

It is the holes which make the cheese. So
says Brillat-Savarin, dubbed the philosopher
of the kitchen, on account of his *Psychologie
du goût* (1825).

320

But consider. For an away game against Italy,
Cantona is dropped. France without
Cantona! Where Cantona should be there is
a hole. France are diminished, surely. The
philosopher of the kitchen stands refuted.

321

And yet. France take the field. Their
opponents face twelve men. Twelve? How is
this possible? They have the legal
complement – plus one. The *absence* of
Cantona. So – can non-existence be? Yes.

322

For example. After a keenly fought game,
Cantona goes to meet his good friend
Chappo in the snug bar of the Goat in
Boots. But Chappo isn't there. The snug bar
at the Goat in Boots reflects back at
Cantona in its every particular the *absence* of
his English friend. The absence of Chappo
is. There is a hole.

323

Equally, there is a hole in the French team
where Cantona should be. You could not
park it in your garage, but it *is*. The
philosopher of the kitchen had a point.

324

And yet when England play without Batto
there is no hole.

325

As his fame spreads, Cantona receives other invitations. He is asked to play in a pro/celebrity football match at Stamford Bridge. He is in two minds. The cause is a good one, and the occasion is to be graced by the Health Secretary, Virginia Bottomley.

326

Cantona is an ardent admirer of Mrs Bottomley. In his opinion, she is the ideal Englishwoman.

327

Haiku 6
'Mrs Bottomley
"Crack on!" "Eat your greens!" "Chin up!"
She's the dog's bollocks.'

328

He turns the invitation down, however. He will not degrade the beautiful game by playing it against comedians and panel-show hosts. And what would the return match be? Competitive shopping at Harvey Nichols? Opening an envelope at an awards ceremony? Anecdotal daytime 'chat' with celebrity chefs and girls who read the weather?

329

His letter of refusal says it all. 'When the fox plays badminton with the goose, the shuttlecock is the loser.'

330

Away to Manchester United. At half-time there's nothing in it. United 0 Leeds 0. By his standards, Cantona has had a quiet game. He has been strangely listless. The last man off the pitch, he is alone as he passes the home team's dressing-room.

331

From within he hears a low, dark, feral
rumble – like a lion on the savannah
gnawing on a carcass. Is this Fergo's team-
talk? He compares it, wonderingly, to the
cool articulateness, the reasonable,
intelligible tones of Wilko.

332

Cantona strives to identify words – specifics,
tactics, changes in the formation – but can
only sense a will and a passion that are
beyond language, that make language
redundant.

333

'Gi an gae wi' a one-tae, fitbaw, laddie . . .'

334

Cantona's heart swells. His fists clench. He
strains his ear to catch more of this
inspirational growling sound.

335

'Nae effin' head tennis, laddie, gae fookin' baw to foo . . .'

336

Cantona feels as if he has put on six inches around the chest. His eyes grow distant. In a daze, he returns to the Leeds dressing-room, but he is now deaf to Wilko's carefully expressed analysis. He has heard the only team-talk that will ever matter.

337

Back on the pitch, Cantona is inspired. He has shaken off his first-half lethargy. After scoring the goal which wins the game for Leeds, he runs instinctively towards the Manchester United fans. They howl with rage and shake their fists. Cantona turns away, smiling.

338
He has found his home.

339
The consumer as a reflection of the inner man. For weeks, Cantona is aware only of a new restlessness within him. He finds himself buying red clothes, a red car, surprising Isabelle by buying red curtains for the drawing-room, signing autographs in red ink. He lingers among the great red behemoths in the Leeds Omnibus Museum, unable to understand his new enthusiasm.

340
He becomes obsessed with the music of Mick Hucknall and Simply Red. Nothing is more important than to win against Manchester City. And, like a distant siren voice, always the muffled snarl of Fergo's team-talk humming in his head.

341

The English sense of humour. On the team
coach, the lads listen to the radio. An 87-
year-old Manchester United fan is being
interviewed on his 60th wedding
anniversary. 'I'll never forget my wedding
day. My Ethel, she looked a picture. After
the reception, we caught the train to
London. It were magic.'
'What's your fondest memory?'
'We stuffed the Arsenal three–none.'

342

To Cantona's surprise, the lads all laugh.
What had been the joke?

343

Small disputes rumble at the club. There is a
growing unease in Cantona's relationship
with Chappo, the big striker. Increasingly,
they run into each other's space. In
Cantona's view, Chappo is leaving him
exposed in the box. 'I'm getting all the
knocks,' he says. 'So I gather,' says Chappo.
They are like two stags, locking antlers,
disputing the same reviving water-hole.

344

A wise man once said: 'A row is never about what it's about.'

345

The players' bar after the game. A discussion about aesthetics. Chappo incessantly hums a tune which, since it hasn't been recorded by Simply Red, Cantona doesn't care for.

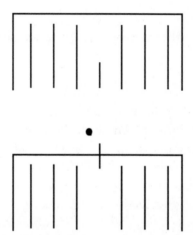

Quantum football: it is not that the small player who soars above those larger than him to score from a corner is more powerful than those around him, but that his imagination reaches beyond theirs to become an uncaused effect beyond the rules of physics.

346
To drown out the big striker, Cantona breaks into song himself.

347
'Every time we say goodbye, I cry a little . . .'

348
'I beg your pardon?'

349
Cantona explains. 'That's a *good* song.'

350
Chappo is unimpressed. 'Really? And who says so, might I ask?'

351
Cantona tries to be reasonable. 'I do.'

352

'I see. And what gives you that right exactly?'

353

Cantona explains. 'In aesthetics we distinguish between a man who knows what he is talking about and one who doesn't. We speak of *educated* taste.'

354

Chappo looks displeased. 'Excuse me, but are you calling me uneducated?'

355

Once again, Cantona tries to explain. 'We do not call a man musical just because he says "aaahhh" when a certain piece of music is played, any more than we call a dog musical if it wags its tail at the same piece of music.'

356

Chappo looks even more displeased.
Strachany, the carrot-topped Scot, tries to
intervene.

357

'Another pint, anyone?'

358

Cantona continues. 'Batto's aged aunt says of
a certain player: "For me, the lad can play a
bit." We're unimpressed. Terry Venables says
of the same player: "In a one-to-one with a
dustbin I'd put my mortgage on the
dustbin." We pay attention. We listen. An
expert has spoken. Some music is better than
other music. Some players are better than
other players. *C'est tout.*'

359

Chappo stands up angrily. 'Look here. You're
talking about me, aren't you, Eric?'

360

Once again Strachany, the wee Scot, tries to
defuse the situation with his ready wit. 'To
be fair, Eric, we try not to listen when
Venners sings "Rhinestone Cowboy" on
karaoke night at Scribes West!'

361

Too late. The big striker has left the bar.
Cantona had been reasonable, but what is
the price of victory if it is gained at a team-
mate's expense? What is the winner left with?

362

Ash in the mouth.

363

A puzzle. In any dispute there are two
victors: he who wins and he who loses.
'Another such victory and I am lost.'

364

The media and the artist. To improve his relationship with Wilko, Cantona agrees at last to speak to the media. But he will not appear on television. Television is for sporting 'personalities' happy to be 'Gotchya'd' in Crinkley Bottom, or for once-proud heavyweights meekly awash in a vat of slime. Cantona will speak only to the press.

365

An interview with a responsible broadsheet can be controlled. He will speak only to the *Independent*, and, from that paper, only to Brian Appleyard, the cross-cultural brain-box of the comment pages. However, like Nabokov before him, he insists that Mr Appleyard's questions are typed out and submitted in advance. He looks forward to a black-belt intellectual tussle with an opponent of the same weight.

366

Away to Chelsea. Outside the ground, large signs have been erected, the sort to be seen at channel ports. 'Welcome.' 'Bienvenue.' 'Wilkommen.' 'Buon Giorno.'

367

The meaning of Chelsea. It is no coincidence that the club's best-known supporters are plump conveyancing solicitors and whey-faced politicians. Chelsea expresses the frustrations of its constituency: the middle-aged mourning their lost youth, the middle-class yearning for the low glamour and hidden violence of the street.

368

Crowd trouble at Stamford Bridge is never caused by the well-behaved younger fans, but by rioting accountants and solicitors, releasing their unexpressed desires.

369

Within every David Mellor, a Dennis Wise is struggling to get out.

370

Another victory. After the game, Cantona is strangely ill at ease. Leeds are seven points clear at the top of the table, but something is missing. Instead of passion, there had been an air of polite complacency among the Leeds supporters. Cantona is left feeling like a matinée actor who has participated in a boulevard comedy nearing the end of a commercially successful run.

371

A childhood memory. A report in the French press of an interview with the great English actor, Lord Olivier. Reference had been made to Olivier's blood-chilling, sub-human howl of despair at the tragic climax of *Oedipus Rex* at the Old Vic. Was it true, the reporter had asked, that Olivier had based it on the terrible, heart-rending cry of a Canadian bull moose caught in a trap? No, Olivier had replied. He had based it on the howl of agonised rage heard on the terraces at Old Trafford when United lost to City.

372

Cantona remembers the swelling crescendo of fury which had greeted his winning goal against United earlier in the season. And, in his ear, still the low, gravelly, metalinguistic growl of Fergo's half-time team-talk.

373

'Nae effin' gggrrrochnaeggggrrrrhhhhh . . .'

374

Surrounded by the lads in the away team's dressing-room, Cantona feels alone. Instead of joining in with the post-match celebrations, he wanders along the King's Road, lost in thought. Nauseated by the Continental emphasis on narcissistic individualism, he had come to England to be part of a team. But Leeds rely all too obviously on his educated skills. Wilko, for all his thoughtfulness, is too caught up in the present. The squad lacks strength in depth.

375

Haiku 7
'Chelsea. Common girls
In short skirts and clever shoes.
Are you carrying?'

376

A coffee bar in the King's Road. Cantona,
still lost in thought, orders a cup of tea. The
room is crowded. He sits at a table already
occupied by a pony-tailed youth and his
pretty, multi-pierced companion.

377

Wilko should be rebuilding the squad.
Institutions can't be scrapped and rebuilt
overnight. Criticism and improvement
should be constant and gradual. Unaware
that he is expressing his thoughts out loud,
Cantona quotes from *The Open Society and
its Enemies*.

378

'You can't rebuild a ship at sea from bow to
stern. At best, you can make small
adjustments here and there.'

379

'Popper?' asks the pony-tailed youth.

380

'Not at the moment, thank you. But if you've got a stash to move, I suggest you try the Arsenal.'

381

In other circumstances, Cantona would have been shocked. But this is Chelsea. What else could one expect?

382

The pony-tailed youth and his multi-pierced girlfriend look bewildered.

383

Haiku 8
'Nice girls like Carol
Vorderman say: *"Mets ça dans
Ton cul!"* to Chelsea.'

384

Back in Leeds, Cantona is cheered by the arrival of Mr Appleyard's questions in the post. This is the intellectual challenge he's been waiting for. He opens the envelope. He reads the questions.

385

1. Who's your fave film star?
2. Who's your fave TV personality?
3. Who's your fave 'character' in a TV soap?
4. What's your fave car?
5. What's your fave food?
6. Who's your fave band?
7. Who's your worst-dressed team-mate?
8. What's your most embarrassing experience!?!?!!
9. What's your –

386

Cantona cannot read on. He throws the questions into the wastepaper basket. He cancels his order for the *Independent*. Henceforth, he'll read the *Guardian*.

387

The psychology of positions on the pitch.
The full back's need above all is to surprise.
Whether his team is in attack or defence, he
has been ignored for so long that his
interceptions (always made for maximum
effect, and at the last second) are widely seen
as heroic – almost as if a spectator has
stepped out of the crowd to make a crucial
tackle. Solipsists on studs, full backs
frequently express their deepest feelings
through practical jokes.

388

On the pitch, he is Le Saux, Dorigo,
Maldini, Irwin. Off the pitch, Robert
Lowell, Jacques Santer, Samantha Janus,
Terry Christian, Vivienne Westwood,
Tallulah Bankhead, Freddie Starr.

389

Leeds win the title. Even at this moment of
triumph, Cantona is oddly out of sorts. His
muse has deserted him again, on and off the
park.

390

The haikus refuse to flow. He throws down his pen and goes to his easel. After a morning's work, he has filled his canvas with a large white egg. With a flourish, he entitles it: 'My life's *oeuf.*'

391

Even as he does so, he realises that it is by such wry disclaimers that the second-rate artist proclaims himself.

392

Cantona throws away his brushes. He hangs his head in shame. Has he brought with him to his beloved England that infection of the soul currently afflicting France? A modish refusal to be serious? He has insulted the whole history of art with an ironic, post-modern, self-deprecating joke.

393

An end-of-season celebration party. Wilko
makes a speech. He thanks Cantona for his
unique contribution to the club's success.
Cantona replies. He uses the occasion to
voice his doubts.

394

Tradition and the individual talent. No
footballer, no poet or artist of any kind, has
his complete meaning alone. His significance
must be seen in relation to the footballers –
to the poets and artists – of the past.

395

'You cannot value me alone. You must set
me, for contrast and comp.'

396

An embarrassed silence, broken by Dorigoey,
the big defender. 'You all right, Eric?'

397

Cantona takes a deep breath. He squares his shoulders. He tries again.

398

'You cannot value me alone. You.'

399

The speech affliction has returned, and it is more serious than before.

400

He takes another deep breath. 'You cannot.'

401

The ever-thoughtful Wilko comes to his assistance. He completes the sentence for him. 'You cannot value me alone. You must set me, for contrast and comparison, among those who went before.'

402

Cantona nods. Wilko continues. '*D'accord.*
But remember this: the necessity that the
new player shall conform, that he shall
cohere, is not one-sided; what happens when
a new team is created is something that
happens simultaneously to the great teams
that preceded it.'

403

'Evidemm.'

404

Wilko continues. 'The great Leeds teams of
the past – Trevor Cherry, Big Jack,
Bremnery, Lorimery – form, as monuments,
an ideal order among themselves. This is
modified by the introduction of new talent
among them. The existing order is complete
before the new order arrives; and so the
relations, proportions, values of each new
talent towards the whole are readjusted; and
this is conformity between the old and the
new. The past should be altered by the
present as much as the present is directed by
the past.'

405
Cantona speaks. 'Anyone fancy a?'

406
Dorigoey. 'First time you've been lost for words, Eric.'

407
Cantona makes a last, herculean effort to complete a sentence. 'The mute greyhound runs faster than the yapping.'

408
'Yeah. Right. Nice one, Eric.'

409
The party continues into the night. Jokes. Good-natured banter.

410
'Here's one, Chappo: 'There was a young man called Flash/Who was bonking a sort called . . .'

411

'THANK you! We'll not have any of that, Dorigoey.' Wilko has intervened just in time.

412

For Cantona, sitting alone at the edges of the party, the celebratory hum grows vague and distant, and is suddenly drowned out completely by that low, gutteral, furious growl, like an old lion gnawing on a carcass, louder now and ever more insistent.

413

'Nae effin' gggrrrochnaeggggrrrrhhhhh . . .'

414

Cantona makes a decision. He will return to France. He will visit the speech therapist who cured him before.

415

The speech therapist's consulting-room. 'I
notice, M. Cantona, that you are wearing a
red shirt, red braces and red socks. Do you
know why?'

416

Cantona shakes his head. He has no idea.
The therapist seems distracted – as if he has
a more important case on his mind. He
stares out of the window. He plays imaginary
golf shots. He doodles on a note-pad. His
mind isn't on the job. Without any great
show of interest, he asks Cantona to describe
his symptoms. Cantona's reply emerges as a
jumble of uncompleted sentences

417

'Leeds. Harvey Nichols. Branch in. Straw
that broke. Gotcha! Boss writing a nov.
Irony. Fave food. Simply Red! Simply Red!
Simply Red! "Every time we say good-bye,
I." Ggggrrrrhhhh . . .'

418

The therapist snaps to attention. He sits bolt
upright. He stops his doodling. He is fully
focused.

419

'Very interesting. Simply Red. Red shirt. Red
braces. Red socks. I think I have the answer,
M. Cantona! Let's try this. Take a deep
breath – that's right – and try to complete
the following sentence: "I, Cantona, wish to
play only for Manchester United!"'

420

'I, Cantona, wish to play only for
Manchester United! I'm cured! It's a miracle!
How much do.'

421
'Merde!'

422
Donc!

423
Manchester United!

424
Before his return to England, he visits his home in the south of France. He meets Le Cochon, the Belgian clogger, who has recently moved here from Auxerre.

425
'How are you doing, then, Eric? Did you hear about the dyslexic English pimp who bought a warehouse . . . ?'

426
Cantona ignores the Belgian bigot. He walks away.

427

What is it that unites Le Cochon's view of
the English – a nation of dullards, as thick
and indigestible as their celebrated bread-
and-butter pudding – and England's glorious
history of achievement, courage and
merciless conquest of countries less
developed than itself? Simple. It is England's
attitude to humour.

428

In Europe, humour is part of life. Politicians,
artists, sportsmen: all aspire to be irreverent,
to be whacky. What is France's most popular
TV programme? The deplorable *Ils pensent
que c'est tout au dessus.*

429

And what are the expressions heard most
often in France? *Tu parles!* (You're joking!)
and *Sans blagues?* (Are you joking?)

430

Why? Because in France no one is taken seriously until he reveals his fundamental lack of seriousness. It is for this reason that French football is a game of zany comedians running in different directions in search of an ever-elusive punchline. After all – where is the joke in teamwork? In victory? In glory?

431

In England humour knows its place. It belongs with the professional jester – men with silly haircuts and shiny suits on television; middle-aged drolls having a sideways look at life in newspaper columns and on the radio.

432

In England, jokes are codified: a comedic view of the beautiful game, for example, is indicated by such phrases as 'sick as a parrot, Brian', 'To be fair, Brian', 'At the end of the day, Brian'. Cantona has already learnt that to make an Englishman laugh and feel at ease, he merely has to add the word 'Brian' to his sentences.

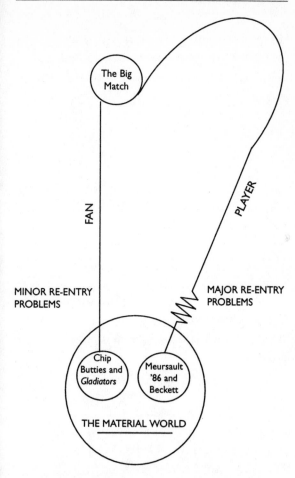

The problem of transcendence. For the fan, a return
to the material world after experiencing a great match
requires an effort of spirit. For the player, the same
journey is an epic voyage of the soul.

433

He recalls an interview with Motty after
Liverpool had been drubbed two-none.
What had been Cantona's careful analysis?
'Possession football is essentially no more
than capitalism at play.'

434

Motty had looked confused. 'But to be fair,
Eric, what about the lad McManamany
then?'

435

Cantona had tried again. 'At the end of the
day, possession football is essentially no more
than capitalism at play, sick as a parrot,
Brian.'

436

The next morning, journalists had enthused
over his comic skills. 'OOH-AH-HA-HA-
HA!' had read the headlines.

437

Consider. The donkey. The hyena. The lion. Two of the three can laugh. But which is the king of the jungle?

438

It was precisely its humourlessness, its courage to be serious, which served England so well in two world wars. Cantona can hardly wait to return. He decides to fly straight to Manchester.

439

He takes his seat on the plane. The seat next to him is empty. Before take-off, a flight attendant offers it to a VIP – a squat, elderly man with a deep, gutteral, German-American accent. Cantona hopes this important traveller won't disturb his flight with small talk.

440

No such luck. Shortly after take-off, the VIP traveller points out of the window. 'Look at those people on the ground. They look like ants.'

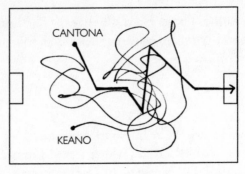

A paradox. A pedometer attached to Keano's foot
has revealed that he covers an average of 23 miles in
a game. By contrast, Cantona rarely covers more
then 800 yards. Yet, in terms of quantum football,
Cantona has travelled further then Keano.

441

Cantona replies. 'An interesting observation.
Surely it was Austin who described the case
of two men watching an American football
match from high up in the stadium. One of
the teams came running on to the field.
"They look like the Miami Dolphins," said
the first man. "They look like ants," said the
second – by which he didn't mean, of
course, that they looked exactly, or even
quite, like ants. For one thing they didn't
have that characteristic nipped-in waist.
Such usages were only of interest, of course,
to ordinary language philosophers at Oxford
in the '50s.'

442

The travelling VIP in the next seat relapses
into silence. No doubt he wishes he'd done
his homework. Cantona is left in peace – to
sleep, to dream of Manchester.

443

Manchester United! Busby's babes! Charlo
and Besty. Stilesy and Buchany. Stepney and
Law. The Doc, who talked like he tackled:
hard but fair. Pat Crerand, the Voice of
Experience. Kiddo, now the first team's
coach.

444

A soccer-mad community! After a
United–City derby, fathers have disinherited
sons, mothers and daughters have come to
blows, Indian newsagents have thrown bricks
through the windows of their own shops.

445

'During the week, Brian, we might get
together with some of the City lads over a
pint, but once we're out on the park, that's
all forgotten.'

446

'Gggggggrrrrrhhhhh . . .' Cantona is coming home. *Cette maison est la mienne!*

447

The first game of the season. Away to Leeds. The team coach: Giggsy and Keano swapping jokes. Brucey and Pallistery playing cards. The Neville brothers pulling faces out of the back window. Fergo on the front seat, reading a copy of *Shoot!*

448

Incey speaks. 'All right, then, Eric?'

449

Cantona smiles. He is content. 'Sweet as a nut, Guv'nor.'

450

After the game, a brief reunion with Wilko. 'No hard feelings, Eric. You won't be easy to replace.'

451

Cantona demurs with grace. 'When the dove falls on the rock, the Father creates another one to make the numbers up.'

452

Wilko nods. They embrace. Cantona turns towards Fergo. 'Papa!' Wilko understands. Fergo remains expressionless.

453

A singular honour! Cantona is invited by Sir Tim Rice to play England's national game at Lord's – the home of cricket. The Lord's Taverners against the Water Rats. The game is to take place in two weeks' time. Cantona equips himself with bat, pads, gloves, white flannels, a book of rules and several volumes on the history of the game. LBW. In-swinger. Wrong 'un. Silly mid-on. 'We'll get 'em in singles, Wilfred.' Cantona will not insult his host by being unconversant with the game's complex rules and arcane skills.

454

At home to Aston Villa. Cantona scores twice. In the players' bar after the game, a discussion about great strikers.

455

Kiddo, the first-team coach, remarks that Tommy Lawton could jump higher than anyone. Fergo, the gaffer, agrees. 'Aye. He seemed to hover in the air.' Pat Crerand, the Voice of Experience, offers an explanation. 'It was discovered that he was anatomically unique. He had an extra bone in his foot. Like a bird.'

456

Cantona considers. The room goes quiet.

457

'To be fair, birds don't fly with their feet.'

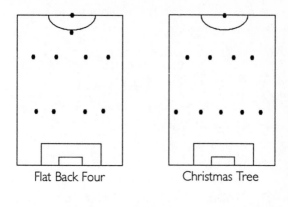

Flat Back Four   Christmas Tree

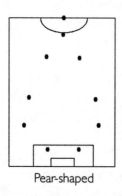

Pear-shaped

Football as the art of compromise. By combining the indigenous flat-back-four formation with the European Christmas tree, English football had gone pear-shaped.

458

Later that evening, the Voice of Experience interviews Cantona for his column in United's programme.

459

'Two cracking goals, Eric. At the end of the day, which one pleased you the most?'

460

'The goal that matters most is the one that I fail to score. Why? Every fulfilment is a slavery. It drives us to a higher fulfilment.'

461

'Fancy another beer, Eric?'

462

But when a man does score a goal, what then does his behaviour tell us? It is a snapshot of the soul.

463

Normal celebrations involve the scoring player falling to the ground and inviting his team-mates to fall on top of him in an ecstasy of congratulation. Here the meaning is simple. In its preparation (delicate, sympathetic, oblique, direct) and in its shattering climax, scoring a goal is akin to the act of love. The players enact an erotic pantomime of dionysian release to confirm their pleasure to the crowd, the opposition and, most importantly, themselves.

464

(The pelvic thrusting at the corner flag, exemplified by the African player Milla, conveys the same message less conventionally.)

465

'Psycho' Pearce in celebration. He stares
angrily into space, every muscle in his body
clenched in triumph and resolve. Jubilant
team-mates bounce off him like hail off a
roof. Even at this supreme moment, he will
not allow himself human feelings. He shows
himself to be beyond emotion. When others
turn to water, he is a rock.

466

Klinsmann in celebration. He dives along
the turf, hair flowing behind him, a broad
grin of self-adoration transfixing his features.
An ironic reference to his reputation as a
diver in the box? Certainly. But, at a more
profound level, he is abasing himself before
the crowd, saying: 'This is not my goal, but
yours.' What is the significance of this? He
will always be leaving clubs: as soon as fans
come to love him, he will desert them. He is
a super-star supplicant, forever seeking new
fans before whom he can abase himself.

467

Ravanelli in celebration. He runs, arms outstretched, mouth in a rictus of ecstasy, shirt pulled over his head. By obliterating the world, he is attempting to rediscover the inner child, the excited little lad whose greatest pleasure was running down the back streets of Turin pretending to be an aeroplane. Closing out the world at this moment is a powerful expression of alienation.

468

Liverpool in celebration. Briefly and affectionately, they grasp the front of each other's shorts like new lovers passing one another at a party. This celebration currently defies deconstruction.

469

And Cantona in celebration? After scoring a
goal, he has been found to grow six inches in
height. He raises his eyes to the back of the
crowd. Occasionally, he assumes a look of
mild astonishment, as if surprised by his
own genius. He is a warrior, victorious after
battle. He is de Gaulle re-entering Paris in
1945.

470

Why does he stand so tall? Because within
him is the pride, the hope, the glory of
millions. He is, during these few seconds,
the football club itself – fan, manager, player,
apprentice, even the silver-haired old lady in
reception. He is the Everyman of the park.

471

The night before the cricket match at Lord's,
Cantona can hardly sleep. Haikus swarm in
his brain.

472

Haiku 9
'Nine down and six to
Win. We'll get 'em in singles,
Sir Tim.' 'Right, Eric.'

473

Haiku 10
'Play up! Play up and
Play the game! Goochy. Lamby.
Bowled by the Frenchman!'

474

Lord's! The home of cricket! At the W.G.
Grace Memorial Gates, he seeks directions to
the pavilion from a man dressed as a duck.
'I'm going that way myself,' says the duck.
He is welcomed by Sir Tim Rice, who is
wearing a dinner jacket and brown suede
shoes.

475

The Lord's Taverners are elderly afternoon celebrities with food down their fronts, a northern chat-show host who has asked for his expenses in an envelope, and a Saturday satirist or two. The Water Rats are composed of summer-show ventriloquists and novelty *artistes*. They are captained by the duck. The umpire is a one-legged saloon bar columnist who is carried to the wicket in a fireman's lift.

476

Cantona, immaculate in flannels, opens the innings with a fat-faced satirist. The umpire's drunk. Cantona takes guard. 'Two leg, umpire, if you'd be so good.' The umpire misunderstands. He thinks Cantona is mocking his misfortune. He takes out his notebook.

477

'What's your name?'

478

'Cantona. What's yours?'

479

The umpire is appeased. 'Cheers, I'll have a double vodka.'

480

The Lord's Taverners are out for 31. The duck takes 7 for 12. Cantona carries his bat for 23. He walks off the field, and keeps walking till he reaches the car park. He climbs into his car and drives back to Manchester.

481

He has participated in a facetious pantomime on the hallowed turf at Lord's. He has disgraced England's national game by playing it with fat-faced funny men and a duck. For his sanity's sake he needs to hear . . .

482

'Nae effin' gggrrrochnaeggggrrrrhhhhh . . .'

483

He's all right now. He's home.

484

The psychology of the pitch. Central defenders. They can be paid no higher compliment than to be told that they 'stopped the other team playing', that they 'cancelled them out'. A negative force, a central defender's talent for obliteration, sometimes leads to problems of empathy in relationships and a tendency to take the philosophy of tough love too literally. They are generally poor conversationalists.

485

On the pitch, Adamsy, Brucey, Pallistery, Keowny, Peacocky. Off the pitch, Pablo Neruda, Queenie Leavis, Norman Tebbit, Jo Brand, Mary Whitehouse, John Birt, Cardinal Hume.

486

United away to Forest at the City Ground. Cantona is inspired. He is in another reality. He goes beyond what is possible. 'For me, Brian, the ball is literally tied to the Frenchman's educated right foot.'

487

Cantona runs at 'Psycho' Pearce, the muscular defender. The crowd roars. 'Ooh aah Cantona!' He nutmegs 'Psycho' Pearce. He puts his foot on the ball and turns through 180 degrees. What's this? He runs towards his own goal!

488

Has Cantona lost his marbles? Consternation among United's fans! He turns again through 180 degrees. He runs at 'Psycho' Pearce. He stops. He stands motionless before him – proudly, as if he has inherited a suit of lights from his Catalan forebears.

489

'Psycho' Pearce is mesmerised. He moves to the matador's music. It is a tragedy in three acts. A swivel of the Frenchman's hips, 'Psycho' Pearce lunges, and begins to fall. His legs lock. He drops to his knees, like a brave bull dying of a broken heart in the afternoon sun.

490

All credit to the lads. The misfortunes of 'Psycho' Pearce are forgotten in the players' bar after the game. 'Psycho' Pearce speaks:

491

'Tell me, Eric. What would you do if you couldn't play football?'

492

Cantona considers. The room falls silent.

493

'I suppose I'd do what you do, Pearcey.'

494

The big defender is satisfied. 'Yeah. Right. Eh?'

495

Yet one day Cantona will be too old to play.

496

He has a dream. The year is 2046. A sleepy village square in rural France. Fat women, laden with local *produits*, return from the market. Old men play *boules*. A bent senior breaks away from the other old men. He watches a group of ragged schoolboys absorbed in a football game. There is longing in the old man's eyes. He tries to join in the game. He kicks a stone, hitting a tree. *'Un nul!'* he cries. The boys are embarrassed. They look away. The old man kicks a cigarette butt through imaginary goalposts. Later, he retrieves it.

497

Football at Manchester United has a different meaning compared to any other club where Cantona has played. There is passion, yes, but it is tempered by a need for every player to come to terms with bigger questions: chaos theory, Heisenberg's Uncertainty Principle, the laws of quantum football.

498

After practice, Cantona spends time in front
of the tactics board, revealing the beautiful
game. Soon, even the older players stay on
to hear his thoughts.

499

'We are in possession. I pass to you. You pass
to me. Nothing has changed, yet everything
has changed. Just as a single dab of paint will
make a masterpiece, or a perfectly deployed
full-stop can create the perfect sentence.

500

'I pass to you. You pass to me. Together we
are creating a 12th man in our team. It is
time itself.'

501

However – the true footballer does not
think; he feels. He does not look; he sees.
Blindfold a great player at any point in the
game and he will tell you where every player
is on the pitch, the speed at which he is
moving and the next five probable passes.
This is not analysis. It is instinct.

502

To create the moment. To step out of time.
To create space from nothing. To be truly
spontaneous. This is the fate of the
footballer. He must be surrealist and realist,
a magician and a scientist – the White
Rabbit one moment, the next the Cheshire
Cat. The footballer is artist, artisan, rebel,
legislator.

503

The pass from Pele to Alberto in the World
Cup of 1970 was as great a work of art as
any line of Rimbaud's. Ballo covering every
inch of grass at Wembley in '66 was worth a
dozen fine cathedrals. Gazza sticking out his
tongue in Italy spoke more eloquently of
anarchy than any tract by Foucault. Moore
snuffing out Rivelino's banana kick in
Mexico created more precedents than
Edmund Burke.

504

In Europe, the bourgeois intellectuals who mock the beautiful game are expressing the middle-class fear of the authentic, of the spontaneous and true. They are displaying a preference for etiquette over inspiration.

At Manchester, class is a meaningless concept on the football pitch. The nicknames 'Bamber' and 'Prof' denote intelligence, and are worn with pride.

505

Waiting for a corner to be taken, Cantona and United's left back, Denis Irwin, sometimes discuss the death of the narrative novel, much to the irritation of Keano, who is an admirer of A.S. Byatt.

506

The psychology of positions on the pitch.
Goalkeepers. The key to their lives is to be
noticed. They would prefer to be blamed, to
be booed off the pitch, than simply to be
ignored. While this can lead to heroics in the
box, it can also provoke acts of comical self-
destructiveness. When a party is being
planned, their names will be first on the
team-sheet, but their restless need to
dominate their area may mean that they end
up alone when the lights are lowered.

507

On the pitch, Schmeichely, Grob, Shaka
Hislop, Oggy Ogrizovic. Off the pitch,
Edith Piaf, Tom Paulin, Camus, Dawn
French.

508

And Cantona? No position on the field of play will entirely satisfy him. He can play them all: outsider, egotist, enabler, solipsist, defender – even goalkeeper. For informal games of five-a-side, Cantona is frequently selected to play in goal ahead of Schmeichely.

509

So where is he most content? In the hole behind the front two. Here, because he is nothing, he is everything; because he is nowhere, he is everywhere.

510
The Psychology of Positions of Play: Dream Team

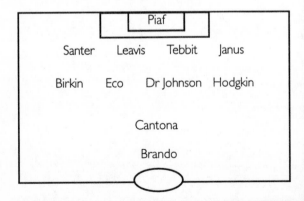

511

A moment of supreme consternation.
Cantona and Isabelle are watching their
favourite television programme, *Our Friends
in the North*. There is an advertising break.
Gary Lineker and Gazza, the *idiot savant*,
appear in humorous mode during an
annonce for potato crisps!

512

The Cantonas look at one another in
astonishment. Not since Jean-Paul Lebeq
promoted haemorrhoid cream on *France-
Inter* with his famous catchphrase, *'Eh, mais
ça va, mon cul!'* have they seen anything like
this.

513

This is worse than the blasphemy at Lord's.
On that occasion, only professional
comedians had been involved. But this . . .

514

Has irony at last entered the soul of his
adopted country?

515

Cantona reaches for the telephone. He rings up Fergo.

516

'Nae effin' gggrrrochnaeggggrrrrhhhhh . . .'

517

All's well. Cantona is himself again.

518

The orgy and *la vie en gris*. Cantona is reading *The Transparency of Evil* by Jean Baudrillard. 'What do we do after the orgy?' asks M. Baudrillard. 'After the moment when modernity exploded upon us, the moment of liberation in every sphere? All we can do is simulate the orgy, simulate liberation. We are obliged to replay the old scenarios precisely because everything has already taken place – from madness and murder to boredom and inanity.'

519

Cantona puts the book down in disgust.
How characteristically French this is with its
thin knowingness, with its world-weary
nihilism. It is the voice of an aristocratic
thief and street addict excusing his own
condition.

520

There is a simple solution which seems not
to have occurred to M. Baudrillard. And
what is this? *Not to have attended the orgy in
the first place* – never to have coupled
publicly with the garish whores of
distraction and celebrity. By turning a deaf
ear to the leering entrepreneurs of chaos and
sensation, the English have maintained their
integrity and seriousness, *la vie en gris.*

521

The true artist finds liberation within the
traditional restrictions of his art.

522
And yet.

523
There has been the shameful comic cricket match at Lord's. And, more seriously, the advertisement for potato crisps featuring Gary Lineker and Gazza, the *idiot savant*. What next? Would *Ils pensent que c'est tout au dessus* be translated into English?

524
Cantona manages to banish such a prospect from his mind. On the field, he excels himself. He and the United fans embark on a glorious love affair, reciprocally inspired. They seem to be free-floating, together but separate, borne upwards by something unknowable, but real. A force. A power. The spirit of the club.

525

So. Does Manchester Unitedness exist?
Leedsness doesn't exist. Take Strachany, the
wee carrot-topped Scot, away from Leeds
and he'd still be Strachany. But what about
Lee Sharpe? Take Sharpey away from
Manchester United and he wouldn't be
Sharpey any more. It happened to Besty.
Besty slogging round the provinces – like a
tipsy old actor whose memory has gone –
wasn't Besty any more. No longer clothed in
the glory of United, he was a vulgar parody
of himself.

526

Cantona has made a second contribution to
the philosophy of social objects. He has
become an ontological collectivist.
Manchester Unitedness *is*. In a world which
no longer contained a living creature,
Manchester Unitedness – like music and
mathematics and the rules of chess – would
still exist.

527

Pat Crerand, the Voice of Experience, speaks:
'To be fair, Eric, Denis Law was still Denis
Law after he moved to City.'

528

'The exception that proves the rule.'

529

'Popper?'

530

'Indeed.'

531

'Thank God. I thought I'd have to try the
Arsenal.'

532

The meaning of Arsenal. The football
stadium as theatre where spectators lay bare
their psyches. During the 1980s, hordes of
cropped-haired inadequates expressed their
inner rage and anxiety by tearing out plastic
seating with their teeth and pushing the
heads of rival fans up the backsides of police
horses.

533

Today? The stands have become a place for
therapy. Fathers bond with their sons. Men
and women attempt to heal relationships.
Middle-aged losers get in touch with their
shadows. Insecurities of class, money and sex
are openly explored during impromptu
group therapy sessions at half-time.

534

Anyone visiting Highbury must have been
surprised by the effects of psychotherapy on
the fans. On all sides one hears cries of 'One
day at a time, Mersony!', 'Honour your own
reality, Wrighty!', 'Expand your own comfort
zone, Platto!', 'Be there for each other, lads!'.

535

Even the chants have a new literary flavour,
with E.M. Forster's 'Only connect!' and
Robert Frost's 'Provide, provide!' being
particular favourites.

536

The need for teams to flatter their supporters
by appearing to be like them. Vinno acts the
saloon-bar psychopath for the Wimbledon
fan. Gazza acts the boozy loon for the Ibrox
faithful. Aware of the newly sensitive,
inward-looking, artistic nature of their fans,
Arsenal insist that once every three months
one of their players goes into addiction
therapy, having first sobbed out a televised
confession to the nation.

537

A night out with the lads at the Rat and
Carrot, Wigan. A stand-up comedian in
cabaret. 'Lager louts have hit on a way of
getting into Wembley. Being picked for
England.'

538

Is this a joke? Can you hear me, mother?
Cantona decides that it can't be. No
Englishman would mock his national team
like this. To his surprise, the lads are
laughing. 'It's half witty, that,' says Sharpey.

539

Hardly. Surely it was Nietzsche who defined
wit as the 'epitaph of an emotion', the fossil
of feeling after feeling has been extinguished.

540

Cantona explains. 'With its debt to
mathematics and music, wit depends for its
effect on an educated audience and shared
assumptions.'

541

'Yeah, right, Eric. Another beer, anyone?'

542

'"All women become like their mothers.
That is their tragedy. No man does. That's
his."'

543
'Your round, Sharpey.'

544
Cantona continues. 'Wit is formal and abstract, which is why we can say a chair, or a haircut, is witty. We might admire the way they play with forms. Humour, on the other hand, is based on character. A humorous chair simply cannot be. To be fair, Sharpey's haircut leaves us baffled.'

545
'Yeah. Right. Eh?'

546

A second moment of consternation.
Cantona and Isabelle are watching BBC2.
David Gower and Gary Lineker, in
blindfolds, are trying to guess the identity of
a celebrity guest – a barrel-thighed forward
from rugby league. Gigglingly, they feel him
up – this super-hero who scored the winning
try against the Wallabies. Two low
comedians, one bald as an egg, the other
unnecessarily bearded, offer a smutty
running commentary. The super-hero from
rugby league retires backstage, looking
suitably embarrassed.

547

Mon Dieu! The virus from France has taken
hold at last in England. *Ils pensent que c'est
tout au dessus* has been translated!

548

It is the nature of comedy to confuse roles.
The vainglorious Falstaff. The solemn
Monsieur Hulot. The self-important hotelier
with his celebrated silly walk. They are
artefacts – created and controlled, and
therefore humorous. And the one thing
which must not be confused? Fiction and
reality. Comedy belongs to fiction.

549

In fiction it might be amusing to see a
donkey dive into a river and attempt to
swim like an otter. In reality, it would be
tiresome.

550

Everywhere Cantona turns, comedy is
spilling out of fiction and into reality.
Politicians appear on shows which exist to
mock politicians. Sportsmen take on joke
roles in feeble quiz shows, vying with career
comedians as to who can vulgarise sport, and
themselves, the most. Comedians are
ubiquitous: on party political broadcasts, in
sports commentary boxes, in newspaper
columns.

551

It is when the chickens cackle loudest that the fox will take his luncheon.

552

When Cantona visits the Rat and Carrot for his pie and mushy peas, there is but one topic of conversation: the lottery. Despair eats into his soul. Even this, the ultimate triviality, has followed him from Europe. The subject of earnest debate and analysis is a game of balls and numbers.

553

The fan and the footballer. They are at opposite ends of the spectrum that is the beautiful game. Each is essential to the other, but discrete. This is what matters. Their difference.

554

And yet. Cantona turns on the television. Two fans are slumped on a sofa, pints of lager resting on their swollen bellies. They are the very picture of fans in a *Match of the Day* stupor. Except for this: these two dead-eyed youths with their leering, sneering half-knowledge of the game present a football show which is more popular than *Match of the Day*.

555

The show? *Fantasy Football League.* Here, by some freakish act of post-modernism, the television screen has turned on itself to become the camera, recording not the achievements of Cantona and others but the slothful, beer-stained events in a dingy bachelor flat. The spectator has become the star.

556

It is as if we were invited to turn away from
Romeo and Juliet to watch two acned
teenagers fumbling in one another's
underwear, the remains of their take-away
curry congealing on the table in front of
them.

557

Graham Greene has said that every serious
novel should revolve around two or three
key conversations. So it is with the artist's
life. In two or three moments of crisis,
cathartic explosions will occur in order to
clear the landscape for further progress.

558

Cantona's first conversation was the match
against Torpedo Moscow, when he tore off
his shirt and stamped on it. What will be his
next conversation, his next defining
moment?

559

Whatever it is, the instrument will be the most eloquent at his disposal: his right foot.

560

The foot that delivers the perfectly weighted ball.

561

The foot that stamped on the Marseilles shirt.

562

The foot that dealt out rough justice to Swindon's Moncur (my heart!) and to Norwich City's Goss (child!).

563

The foot that will carry the argument against irony into the stand at Selhurst Park.

564

Away to Crystal Palace. After a routine tussle with Palace's right back, Cantona is sent off. Like a drowning man, a player shown a red card sees his footballing life flash before him. Effort. Dreams. Training. Injury. Hope. Glory. Despair. For those few seconds, he is caught between pitch and stand – no longer a player, not yet a spectator. He is uniquely vulnerable.

565

As he walks towards the tunnel, he experiences his whole life in football. The back streets of Marseilles, stamping on his shirt against Torpedo Moscow, Le Cochon, red-faced and inarticulate, Wilko and his novel, Motty, camaraderie on the team coach ('All right, Eric?' 'Sweet as a nut, Guv'nor'), Fergo, 'Fookingghhhhrr . . .'

566

His memories are a barricade against the tornado of human sound that is breaking all around him.

567

Du calme, du calme. He tries to speak. 'The leopard who hunts alone will soon. The leopard who. The.'

568

Someone is screaming in his ear. A fan. Almost on the pitch, his finger stabbing the air, veins throbbing in his neck. Cantona pauses.

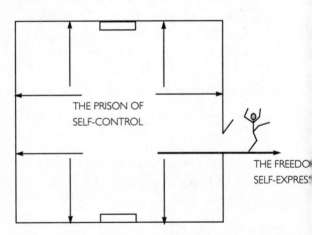

THE PRISON OF
SELF-CONTROL

THE FREEDO
SELF-EXPRES

The Selhurst paradox: only by escaping the prison of
the self can man become himself.

569

The man invites him to return to France. He implies an inappropriate relationship with his mother.

570

The barricade breaks. New images fill his head. Vinno and Fash. Celebrity haircuts. The two beer-stained yobs on the sofa. Football bloopers of the year. The stone-bald comedian feeling up the rugby player. Sir Rice. The duck. The fat-faced satirist. Flushed politicians stooging for low comedians. *Have I Got News for You?* The lottery. Linford's lunch-box. Sequinned Gladiators. *Ils pensent que c'est tout au dessus.*

571

Cantona breathes deeply. Destiny beckons. How best to demonstrate the hollowness of a sport where the footballer and the fan, the serious and the comic, have been confused by the demon of post-modernism?

572

He has the answer. He will become a fan, join the crowd, act like them, cross the barrier between player and spectator. He will demonstrate the emptiness of disorder.

573

Cantona lets his right foot do the talking.

574

There are no great crimes of which an intelligent man does not feel capable. According to Gide, great minds do not yield to them *because they would then restrict themselves.*

575

Cantona has yielded. He has restricted himself. Charged with assault, he will be judged now, not by other poets and philosophers, but by Mrs Jean Pearch of the Croydon Magistrates Court.

576

Fergo and the lads stand by him. Even
Vinny Jones offers himself as a character
witness. Cantona thanks him, but declines
the offer.

577

'A goose should not be of the jury at a fox's
trial.'

578

Proud and upright in the dock, Cantona
quotes Rousseau in his defence.

579

'As you will be aware, Mrs Pearch, Rousseau
recommended assassination for reasons of
honour. "A blow or an insult received and
endured has social effects that no sage can
forestall, which can be avenged by no
tribunal. The offended person becomes the
sole magistrate, the sole judge between the
offender and himself; he owes himself justice
and he alone can render it to himself."'

580

Mrs Pearch asks Cantona whether he has anything else to say before she sentences him.

581

Cantona replies. 'Just this. The heron is all too often blamed for the hedgehog's misdeeds. You'll know about goldfish, Mrs Pearch.'

582

'Six months,' says Mrs Pearch.

583

Incey speaks. 'You got a result there, Eric.'

584

On appeal, the sentence is reduced. Instead of a prison term, Cantona must do six months' service in the community.

585

Cantona has travelled Europe from Auxerre to Nîmes, from Leeds to Manchester, in search of the elusive butterfly of self. And where does he find it?

586

At the Community Resource Centre in Ellesmere Park, coaching schoolboys.

587

The most important role on the pitch? Provider. Only with the Ellesmere Park Juniors does Cantona begin to understand. The true artist must provide – not just with his play, but with his words, his actions, his life. This is his destiny.

588

Cantona is a teacher now. And not merely on the park. Off the park, he has plans to expand his pupils' understanding. To celebrate the end of his suspension, he will mount a production of Beckett's *Souffle* upstairs at the Rat and Carrot, Wigan.

589

The choice is a wise one. The play has a
small cast and is one of Beckett's shortest.
Indeed, it hasn't got a cast at all, and it lasts
for only 30 seconds. It will not unduly tax
the attention span of the lads from United
and the boys from Ellesmere Park. He will
also invite Fergo, Wilko, Cloughie, 'Psycho'
Pearce and many others.

590

Returning one afternoon from the
Community Resource Centre, he puts in a
call to Wilko.

591

'Do you remember that conversation we had
about football's essential verb?'

592
'Do what?'

593

Cantona explains. 'It is neither *être*, "to be",
nor *avoir*, "to have". It is "to give". *Donner
est vivre.*'

594

The Leeds manager replies with a curt suggestion.

595

Cantona invites him to the first night of *Souffle* nonetheless.

596

That night, he works on his production of *Souffle*, deciding, for the sake of narrative drive, to make some judicious cuts. He takes out three seconds at the beginning and two seconds at the end.

597

Ainsley Parrott, a talented ten-year-old playing for Ellesmere Park Juniors, shyly approaches his hero after a coaching session. From his training bag, Ainsley produces a photograph of Cantona. He asks him to sign it.

598

The old Cantona would have signed it with a flourish. The new Cantona tears the photograph in half and hands it back to the astonished child.

599

Cantona explains. 'Bring me a photograph of Ainsley Parrott. That I will sign. Heroes are for fans, not for players. There are many Cantonas today. There's only one Ainsley Parrott.'

600

Under their temporary coach, Ellesmere Park Juniors reach the play-offs of the Lancashire Under-11 league. Ainsley Parrott scores a goal, but the 73-year-old referee awards a penalty for excessive celebration, followed by a second penalty for dissent. The lads finish second in the league.

601

After the game, Ainsley's schoolmates offer to let down the tyres of the referee's car. Ainsley's reply says it all.

602

'Where the windmill turns most freely, the waterlily seldom grows.'

603

It is from the ashes of sacrifice that the loveliest flowers bloom. The Selhurst Park conversation, the trial before Mrs Pearch, the days spent at the Ellesmere Community Centre: Cantona's soul blossoms in the ashes. There are reports in the newspapers that he is tired of England and will soon be signing for Inter Milan. The opposite is true.

604

Cantona has come home. Not to England, nor even to Old Trafford. He has come home to himself.

605

The first night of Beckett's *Souffle* upstairs at
the Rat and Carrot. In the front row –
Fergo, expressionless in black tie with Mrs
Fergo, Cloughie, 'Psycho' Pearce, Wilko,
with a copy of the text on his knee, Incey,
the Guv'nor, and the other lads, and Ainsley
Parrott with his mum and dad. Expectations
run high. The play, with its cuts, will only
last for 25 seconds, during which a breath is
drawn and exhaled, accompanied by a 'faint,
brief cry'. But will the audience be gripped?

606

The curtain goes up on an empty stage.

607

The sound of an exhalation. 'Sssss . . .'

608

Ten seconds. It's going well. In the audience
you could hear a pin drop.

609
'Sssssss . . .'

610
Fifteen seconds! Rapt silence in the house.

611
'Sssssss . . .'

612
Twenty seconds!

613
'Sssssss . . .'

614
'Anyone fancy a beer?'

615
The Guv'nor has had enough. Cantona
blames himself. His cuts had been too
radical. Still, the great artist must dare to
fail. Beckett would have understood.

616

For months Cantona has not kicked a
football. He has been redefining his
relationship with the ball, with the game
and, above all, with himself. Returning to
The Cliff training ground, he explains to
Fergo and his team-mates that he has
undergone a soul change. Maybe he is not
physically fit, but in his heart he is fitter
than he has ever been. Perhaps he has lost a
yard of pace, but his spirit has taken him
beyond speed and strength to another place.

617

He reminds Fergo of the French phrase,
reculer pour mieux sauter. To step back in
order to jump better.

618

'Ye can *recule*, laddie,' growls Fergo. 'But nae
sae much of the *sauter*-ing this time, dae ye
ken?'

619

Cantona smiles. By the end of the first
practice, he has been made team captain.

620

It is not the strongest or the fastest lion
which leads the pride, but the one who
wears his scars with the most dignity.

621

Captaincy. What is it? The art of being, of
having, of *giving*. The second-rate captain
urges, punches the air with his fist, ruffles
the hair of the younger players in a
pantomime of affection and concern. The
true captain says nothing. He leads with his
soul.

622

The role of the parent? To give children a
sense of belonging. In the summer, Cantona
has bestowed this gift upon the Ellesmere
Park Juniors; now, in the autumn, he brings
it to the younger players at The Cliff.

623

Scholesy, Beckhamy, the Neville brothers,
Butto: each has talent, but is isolated by the
loneliness of youth. Individual figures, they
become part of the whole picture when
Cantona is playing.

624

Cantona's return. At home to Liverpool. To accentuate the importance of unity, of family, Cantona has invited his father, Albert, to watch the game.

625

How best to lead with the soul? How best to provide a landscape for the young and talented? To set the stage for them.

626

After 67 seconds, Cantona has his chance. In a position to score himself, he threads a perfectly weighted ball through to the young lad, Butto. Butto scores.

627

It is the goal which causes Cantona the most pleasure in his whole career.

628

The year is 2047. A sleepy provincial square in rural France. Old men play *boules*. One of the old men hesitates before his turn. He is lost in thought. His head is full of memories of another land, another time.

629

'Move along the bus, please!' Mrs Bottomley.
Bolloms the same-day cleaners. 'They'll be
ready on Thursday.' Decency, honour, thin
August sunshine on the slumbering Thames.
'All right, clever bollocks.' Tripe and onions.
Mushy peas. Mr Kipling and his cakes.
'Nicole?' 'Papa!' Sally Gunnell. Mother's
Pride. 'Search for the hero inside yourself.'
Anyone fancy a beer? Motty, Fergo, Wilko.
The young lads Beckhamy and Butto –
grandfathers themselves long since. The
Guv'nor. Vinno. Mrs Pearch. The goal that
won the cup in '96. Gotcha! Crinkley
Bottom. 'Rock on, Tommy!' 'It's good to
talk.' Big ships pulling away into the
distance, low horns moaning. A murmur of
doves above a cathedral close. 'Go home,
French mother-fucker!'

630

The old man's eyes fill with tears. Will he
always remember? Perhaps not. Old men
forget.

THE AUTHORS

Terence Blacker was born in Leicester in 1942. The first
graduate of Reading University to be offered a traineeship
at the BBC, he worked on several programmes, including
In Town Tonight, and met his first wife, Jennifer Miles, now
an independent producer. In 1973, he left the BBC to teach
in the Gender Studies faculty at Thames Valley University.
While researching the influence of Enid Blyton, he met Dr
Gillian Birkett, with whom he later set up home until
1982, when Dr Birkett moved to America with their two
children. A part-time tutor at the University of East Anglia,
Blacker is an avid enthusiast of trad jazz and has recently
taken up the clarinet.

His publications include *Partners in Apartness: A
Programme for Positive Divorce, Dad! Fatherhood in Prose and
Poetry* (editor), *Who Did You Say Was Calling?: Parenting from
a Distance* and *Alone and Just Fine: A Guide to Mid-Life
Independence*.

William Donaldson was born in South London in 1953.
From 1971 to 1976 he studied Philosophy at the University
of Warwick, later publishing in book form his PhD thesis
Shooting the Wrong Donkey: Sense and Sensibilia Refuted
(Routledge and Kegan Paul, 1978). He continued his
studies at the University of California, achieving, in 1980,
the distinction of being the first Englishman to appear in
the Rose Bowl as a starting quarter-back. Dr Donaldson
now lives in Norwich with his life partner Jeremy Bevin, a
regular on *The Antiques Roadshow*, and is Reader in
Aesthetics at the University of East Anglia.

Apart from his academic publications, he has contributed
articles on style, pop music and fashion to the 'Real Life'
pages of the *Independent on Sunday*. He is currently working
on a documentary series for Channel Four, *The Tactics of
Ingratiation: The New Man in Modern Fiction*.